One Bone at a Time

Tales of an Adventurous
Animal Chiropractor

Alison Seely

Ottawa Canada
crowecreations.ca

First Crowe Creations edition August 2019
crowecreations.ca

Interior design by Crowe Creations
Text set in Times New Roman; headings set in Calibri Light

Cover design © 2019, Deb Ozarko, debozarko.com
Cover vector art sourced from Vecteezy.com
About the author photo, © Deb Gleason
Back cover photo, © 2019, Deb Gleason, debgleason.net
Final page cartoon, ©, "An amalgam of work by Scott Mooney and Jess Clouthier"

Crowe Creations
ISBN: 978-1-927058-59-6

3 4015 07229 5635

To Kev—my Rock and best friend.

Foreword

THIS BOOK IS A WORK of non-fiction, insofar as non-fiction is possible with the vagaries of opinion, memory, and time. Memory may be less than robust, particularly after the number of concussions I've suffered, details of which you will glean if you have the stamina to read the entire book. Friends and family are named because they would be impossible to disguise.

Clients and patients are renamed, and some details modified or stories amalgamated, to protect some modicum of patient privacy. I am immensely grateful to my editorial unpaid staff of Kevin, John, Jane, Marc, and Deb. Sherrill Wark was invaluable in bringing the manuscript from an iPad file to a fully fleshed book. My three children, Savannah, Forest, and Logan were consistent supportive cheerleaders. Kevin was unstinting in buttressing my insecurities as a writer and egging me to bring this work to a public audience.

And I am so grateful to my parents who fostered my love of reading, my self-confidence as a scientist and writer, and encouraged me to see the best in people and the opportunity in setbacks.

Table of Contents

Career Choices

THE FIRST EUREKA MOMENT CAME in a darkened converted warehouse where I housed my research animals.

The cornea was moist and firm as I prodded it gingerly with my finger. I flinched, but there was no responding movement from the eye.

"What do you think?" The query came from Kev in a stage whisper. "Is she dead?"

Kev had accompanied me to the Annex. He was a chiropractic student, had no love for the smell of fish or seal faeces, but was my staunch supporter, partner, best friend, and eventual husband.

Whispering made little sense. We were alone in the cavernous zoo annex at the University of Guelph. The hum of the circulating water in the giant aquaria which housed the seals was a constant background noise. There were no lights except for an eerie blue glow from the X-ray view boxes which projected pictures of Weddell seals and Hooded seals on ice floes. Neither Kev nor I had been able to find the overhead lights in the darkness. The eerie setting seemed to invite whispering.

"I really don't know" I stage-whispered back. "Maybe she's just in a dive."

We had elected to do a late night check on Zoe, one of my twenty-one grey seals we had taken from Amet Island in Nova Scotia for a reproductive study as part of my PhD thesis. Remarkably, twenty of the seals adapted well and were eating thawed herring and thriving in outdoor aquaria in the arboretum at the university. One female, Zoe, had not thrived in captivity. She steadfastly refused to eat dead herring, and we had taken to force-feeding her the fish which were stuffed with a variety of vitamins and appetite stimulants. Zoe now had an hourglass silhouette, with ribs and hips showing. Not a healthy look for a seal.

Zoe was hauled out beside the tank, with no obvious signs of respiration. I couldn't trigger a blink response. I tried to persuade myself she was in a deep-dive physiology where her heart would slow to several beats per minute, and she could breath-hold comfortably for over twenty minutes. But the eye was unresponsive, and she was feeling unnaturally stiff.

"I think she must be dead," I conceded, dejected. We bagged her and moved her to the freezer. I would do the autopsy the next day.

I felt absolutely wretched. I had spent the last few weeks in a vigil with Zoe, trying to tempt her to eat by putting herring fragments into her mouth. I would drag dead herring in front of her in the water with dental floss wrapped around the gills, trying to mimic lifelike fish motions. I even batted her nose with the fish so she would aggressively bite at it. But nothing seemed to work and Zoe was steadfast in her refusal to eat.

Unlike Zoe, the other twenty seals in my study quickly learned that the thawed frozen fish was nutrition. As a result, they all regained their vitality and typical seal fusiform shape. Zoe's resistance to all my feeding efforts eventually led to starvation.

I had twenty-one grey seals under my care at the University of Guelph. I had captured the seals on the ice floes in Nova Scotia in a Rambo styled expedition. We had captured the six males and fifteen females by throwing large nets over their bodies and then attaching the nets to a waiting helicopter. We then carried them swinging under the helicopter to the mainland where we loaded them into a ten-ton 18-wheeler. We drove through the night and unloaded the seals into tanks in the arboretum on Guelph campus. It was a harrowing journey and dramatic change of scenery for the seals. It was probably more surprising that twenty of the seals had adapted, than the fact that Zoe had not.

Putting my seal subjects through such an upheaval had a lofty aim. Seals were being blamed for a crisis in the cod fishery and there were strong lobby groups hoping to reintroduce a seal cull, a honeyed term for clubbing baby seals on the head. Grey seals are aquatic mammals, generally safe from human predation in their ocean environment. Once a year, they haul up on fast ice or beaches to deliver a pup and then nurse for three weeks, mate, and then return to the ocean. The pups transform from skinny creatures in baggy skins to bulging vulnerable blimps on a diet of fifty-three-percent-fat seal milk. They can easily be hunted during this phase before they learn to manoeuvre into the safer sea. Maternal investment ends at three weeks.

This three-week window of accessibility gave me the means to capture the twenty-one seals I required for my thesis project. I was studying reproduction in seals. The seals have a natural embryonic development of around nine months, much like we do. They have evolved a mechanism of minimizing predation by pairing the whelping and breeding season by a feature called embryonic diapause which extends the pregnancy to eleven and a half months. The fertilized egg develops to a multi-celled blastocyst and then floats in the uterus without implanting for three months. I was investigating whether an injection of Depo-Provera, a human long-acting birth control pill, could prevent conception or implantation of the fertilized egg. I hoped to spare future generations of clubbed seals by controlling the number of pups born every year.

I was enamoured with my research aims, and also looking forward to establishing the basic biology of the hormone controls of delayed implantation. The research might save the lives of thousands of seals. Zoe's demise still felt unacceptable. I cried as I left the building that night, feeling exhausted and guilt-ridden.

It was not the first time I found that my empathy for the subject challenged my allegiance to the research question. I had started my PhD in California where I was part of a research team attempting to attach dive recorders to Fin whales. Every time my colleague aimed his darting gun and scope, however, I would start muttering "jinx" under my breath. I had to be very surreptitious—like being a visitor in the stands of a home game for basketball, willing the local player to miss the free throw. I was supposed to be on the home team, the team of researchers. But my loyalties were with the animal, not the scientists.

I opted for a career in marine biology for a very animal-centred reason. I was truly happiest when I was in the company of animals. Ironically, I was desperately allergic to mammals. I had reasoned that perhaps I could work with animals without dander, those residing in the ocean.

Despite my allergies, I had always gravitated toward dogs and cats when visiting friends. They seemed to reciprocate my affections. In a room filled with people, the dog would inevitably elect to rub against my leg, while the cat would jump in my lap. I even seemed to be singled out by working dogs who were trained to be impervious to distractions. On a backpacking year around Europe, I was twice approached by a tail-wagging border dog. My bags were emptied in embarrassing detail with tampons, birth control pills, and dirty underwear laid out for inspection while they searched for drugs to no avail. On both occasions, I was told the same thing: the dogs never make mistakes. If displaying tail-wagging affection was not considered "a mistake", the border folks were indeed correct.

The attention from dogs in confined spaces in a Ventolin-free era sometimes meant visits to the hospital emergency ward to be hooked up to oxygen. As a youngster, I would spend sleepovers at a friend's house gasping for air at an open window—even in arctic winter conditions—because of my allergy to her German shepherd.

Working with mammals was clearly not an option. But hairless mammals? Dolphins? Whales? Even seals? These seemed to be a viable alternative. I started my studies at Scripps Institution of Oceanography in San Diego before continuing my PhD at the University of Guelph when my Canadian funding dictated that I stay in Canada for the studies. Despite being a landlocked centre, I had Natural Sciences and Engineering Research Council of Canada (NSERC) funding to bring seals to the Guelph facility for a three-year research study into the endocrinology of their reproduction.

The autopsy on Zoe was performed the following morning by myself and a vet from the department of exotic animals from the Ontario veterinary college. The obvious culprit was confirmed. There were zero fat stores, including no subcutaneous fat and no interstitial fat. Zoe had starved to death. I mourned being the cause, but was otherwise riveted by assisting the veterinarian with the necropsy. I poured over Zoe's insides, palpating her shrunken organs with gloved hands, cutting slices of the ovaries for histology, and marvelled at the size and colour of her diving lungs. This part of biology fascinated me.

The second phase of my eureka-career game-changer came about one week later. I was dressed in my Jane Fonda best: leggings, thong unisuit, and leg warmers. I was enrolled in classes at Gold's Gym in town. It was the '80s and aerobics ruled.

While at the gym one day, I happened to observe one of the instructors who had recently finished teaching her class. Freshly showered with clean hair wrapped in a towel, she opened her locker, sniffed her clothes and glowered. "Ugh. No way can I get dressed in these again." She chose instead to put her sweaty aerobic outfit back on.

"What are you doing, Claire?" her friend asked, laughing. "You'll have to wear them eventually."

"I'll just work out until I'm warm enough to go out with these clothes," she responded. "My jeans stink like pig shit. We had swine rotation today. Those are not touching my skin until they've been through the laundry!"

Claire was clearly a veterinary student. Guelph has one of the five Canadian veterinary colleges in Canada. I encountered scads of vet student wannabes in the classes I proctored in the biology department. But I did not, however, know any students currently in the program.

I watched her retreating back while experiencing a strange sensation. I disliked her? I admired her? I resented her? I couldn't name the unfamiliar but nasty emotion. Then I realized: I was envious. It was a novel and uncomfortable feeling, one I knew I had to address.

The next day, I tackled it head on. I called the Y and signed up for an aerobic instructor's class.

And I applied to vet school.

A History with Animals

My parents probably sighed with relief when I opted to enter a clinical field. Academia is a not a dishonourable profession but my family uniquely knew medicine. Both my parents and eventually one sister and one brother all chose medicine. My youngest brother did not stray far from the family path and became a naturopathic doctor. My mother calculated that she was the twelfth in her immediate family to pursue a career in medicine.

When I was old enough to finally voice an opinion, I was repeatedly asked to defend my decision to not pursue medicine. "Are you going to be a doctor just like your mommy and daddy?" friends of my parents would ask in the saccharine tones one uses on kids when they don't really anticipate an answer.

"Nope! I want to be a ballerina, jockey, actress, marine biologist ..." the answer morphed with my age and passions, but it consistently repudiated medicine. I disliked the smells of hospitals, the claustrophobic feeling of the long corridors, and the bustle of too many people.

This antipathy was cemented when I spent two weeks in the hospital at the age of seven. I had gotten my hand tangled in the machinery of an escalator and I almost lost three fingers. The mangled hand required a hundred and twelve stitches to reconstruct it. I was confined in the children's hospital for two weeks, likely the standard stay during the heyday of social medicine in the early '70s. Although much of the care was probably excellent, I hated my time there. I was meant to be a voiceless demo for teaching students who talked over my bed, debating the likelihood of my regaining enough dexterity to write. I remember a conversation about a bad date night as the orderlies wheeled me to surgery. And, of course, the food I was served deserved the infamous reputation it is well-known for. One nurse even threatened me with a huge needle to give me blood if I didn't eat my full meals.

I still hate hospital teal green and the smell of rubbing alcohol and iodine. I wasn't keen on anything to do with people either. When I put together my photo album as a preteen, I meticulously cropped humans out of the pictures. The album consisted uniquely of landscapes, mountains and oceans, and horses, dogs and sheep.

We used to travel to Scotland to visit my mother's family cottage in the far north in Sutherland. I converted a woodshed into an 8′ × 6′ miniature bedroom furnished by a tolerant and loving grandfather. One morning, I found an abandoned, still-wet newborn lamb curled up behind a rock in the fields dividing our croft from the ocean. I gathered her up, tucked her in my sweater and trudged up the hill. I brought her to my woodshed oasis where I cleaned her and warmed her with my mom's hairdryer. For two days, I spoon fed her a diet of cow's milk before she was discovered, getting skinnier and more sickly by the day.

My aunt, an eccentric animal-loving spinster and farmer, was recruited to help with the care of the lamb. I learned how to bottle feed colostrum, and then milk harvested from another ewe. Moira taught me how to identify the gender of the lamb that I named "Canella". Fortunately for Canella, she was a female. A male, I was told, would have a dismal future with a meat-market destiny in the fall. I reluctantly parted with Canella, a thriving energetic lamb, at the end of the summer holiday in Scotland. Moira reassured me that Canella would be a mom the following summer and would not be a candidate for mutton roast.

Horses were always a passion of mine. In fact, I was quite typical with that particular obsession. When I was studying at Scripps and shifted from working with fish to seals, my advisor scathingly commented, "from horses, to seals, to dolphins, heh? Such a cliché." His research focused on electric fish—a passion I quickly discovered I didn't share. I never did graduate to dolphins, but he was close to the mark in identifying my interests.

When I was six, my allergies became a potential obstacle to time with horses. My mother made it clear that if I tested negative for horse allergies, I could have the horseback riding lessons I longed for. I was subjected to the crude, medieval allergy testing of the time. It involved the barbaric testing of various allergens deposited in tiny holes along my arm, made with a hooked implement that resembled a sharpened crochet needle. I asked which particular hole in my pin-cushioned arm was horse serum. I circled it with blue ink, as well as the one for hay which the technician kindly identified for me. Sadly, the site of dog serum erupted into something resembling a bubonic boil. I also fared poorly with dust, eggs, chocolate (sadly), tomatoes, and oranges. The horse site remained as flat and unresponsive as I had willed it to be, and the riding lessons I was promised appeared on my immediate gleeful horizon.

My first riding lesson placed me in the company of seasoned girls who seemed much older and more experienced than I. Sporting jodhpurs and hard hats, they were already adept at picking horse feet and tacking up. I bounced my way through the hour-long class with my horse, "Harold", alternating between a grumpy trot and pausing to pull me over the pommel to eat grass. I was a bony twig of a kid with little between my sitz bones and the saddle. I sported a pair of matching raw buttock cheeks after the first lesson.

Regardless, I was undaunted, and counted down the days to the second lesson. After seeing the painful result of my first riding lesson, my mother rose to the challenge and padded a pair of underwear with medical gauze and cotton padding. I wore them throughout the first season. They were stained with serum from the oozing sores until I developed a seat and the ability to post.

I continued to ride through my teenage years, becoming a passionate three-day eventer, limited only by the lack of a horse to my name. My Christmas list of "horse, palomino, chestnut, mare, stallion, gelding, bay, bronco …" was a scourge to my parents. Although I never got the begged-for horse, I was well-gifted in grooming tools, Best of the West miniature horses, and books on horses.

Nicole, our stern, British riding instructor, told us we could consider ourselves accomplished horse back riders when we had fallen one hundred times. I gullibly took this to be fact. I meticulously documented every fall with the precision of an accountant, drawing the horse in question, the type of fall, and the date. I believe the final tally was sixty-seven.

In the absence of a horse to call my own, I worked with facsimiles. My parents surprised us one Christmas with a miniature poodle, named "Holly", for the timing. She was meant to be a hypoallergenic solution to our desire for a dog. Unfortunately, she was neither fully hypoallergenic, nor really big enough to qualify as a dog. I did make her my horse for a while, and I taught her to respond to walk, trot, and canter commands.

I had a banana bike which granted me the freedom to easily navigate the streets of Montreal. With the casual parenting typical of the '70s, my parents' only requirement was that I present myself at home by supper. I called my bike "Star" and would post my way down the streets. I adopted a jumping position to mount curbs and would gently pat Star on the shiny frame after a well-executed jump.

My bedroom was a testament to the obsession. Half the room was converted into a Best of the West panorama with horses in the paddocks, a barn and ranch house made of papier maché, and hand-painted chopstick jumps covering the floor. I covered one of the horses with leftover false fur from a jacket my mother had made, and used a cut-off toothbrush to groom "Scout" regularly. I eagerly looked forward to bedtime when I could shrink myself to a size proportional to that of the plastic horses and continue my fantasy in the dream world. My dreams would come to life with my shrinking and I would be able to ride all night long.

A career with animals seemed self-evident. I discovered the world of marine biology in the form of a small paperback in my high school library, titled *Dangers of the Sea*. It made great sense for me to work with animals who didn't shed hair. I chose Acadia for my undergrad based on its imagined proximity to the sea. Although it turned out to be mudflats, not ocean, in its back yard, it was the perfect choice. I had a clear career vision which led me right up to that pivot point with the grey seals.

The decision allowed me to rekindle an idea I'd abandoned as a teen. We had a collection of well-worn, dog-eared paperbacks by James Herriot at the family cottage, that I had never allowed myself to read, not wanting to be teased with an unachievable dream.

When I received my letter of acceptance from the Ontario Veterinary College at Guelph, I couldn't wipe the grin off my face. I also finally allowed myself to read the entire James Herriot series over the next few weeks.

Ontario Veterinary College

THE TRANSITION TO VET SCHOOL turned out to be faster than anticipated. I ran into a thesis roadblock with a member of my advisory committee who insisted the female seals all be euthanized for reproductive histology. I point-blank refused. One professor argued that I needed results from the ovary histology to confirm the pregnancy status of the females. I countered with a proposal to radiograph them to check for foetuses. The compromise meant demoting the PhD to a Masters so the seals could be released back to the wild at the conclusion of the study. Although it was a hard-won victory against vigorous opposition from my advisor, he did a smooth about-turn when interviewed by the press regarding our research. He announced that it was only humane and right to return our subjects to the wild when our agenda was clearly about preventing needless death in seals. I was happy with the result even if it meant smiling in agreement as his mouth voiced *my* words.

What this meant was that I could complete the first of the five-year veterinary program while completing my Masters. Although I felt like a granny with an anticipated graduation age of thirty-one, I quickly discovered that the age range of my fellow hundred students was from twenty-one to forty-nine. The eldest in the class was short, grey haired and pudgy; truly grandmotherly. She had a pragmatic approach of declaring that the five-year program would make her either a fifty-four-year-old vet tech or a fifty-four-year-old vet, depending on her choices. It was a refreshing contrast to the number of times I have heard, "Oh, I wish I'd become a vet but …"

We were fifty-six women and forty-four men, the beginnings of a relatively recent shift from a male-dominated field. The ratio continued to skew toward females in subsequent years. I believe the current ratio is closer to 8 : 1. The gender shift in my years at the Ontario Veterinary College meant that most courses were taught by men, sometimes with a pronounced avuncular tone; other times, completely sexist. It was the end of an era for a male-dominated profession. One memorable lecture on endocrinology had the middle-aged professor detouring to discuss breast-feeding.

"If it's done right, it never hurts," he proclaimed. "If it hurts, you girls just don't know what you're doing. The whole areola must be in the child's mouth!"

"And …" he paused meaningfully, "I probably shouldn't say this, but most of you girls don't know how to properly stimulate your men either. The penis is most sensitive on the tip, not the shaft." We rolled our eyes, but neither commented nor complained. This was thirty years before the Me Too Movement.

The women who taught were dynamos: forthright, intimidating, and highly skilled. They were not immune to sexual discrimination from clients, however.

One belligerent horse trainer refused to address the female head of equine surgery directly. "Bring out the doctor," he demanded. "I will not talk to this groom!"

The surgeon angrily walked out of the room leaving the young male intern to deal with the nasty client.

Based on general seating choices, the class fractured into groups. There were the "keeners" who sat eager faced in the front row. At the back of the class were the relaxed hecklers with feet balanced on the seats in front of them. They were generally smokers who were more interested in cow medicine. I made quick friends with a group who opted for mid-way seating on the right side of the auditorium. This afforded late arrivals and early departures. We would collaborate on group projects, problem-based learning modules, and fun evening outings. Two of the girls, Jiffy and Christina, were kindred spirits with wild, untamed blonde hairdos, a passion for exercise, and a general indifference to public opinion. We became fast friends and still meet regularly for athletic races and social weekends.

Veterinary College did not herald the end of animal welfare conflicts. The program offers an interesting juxtaposition of animal loving and animal use. Students are counselled to avoid talking about loving animals in their application interviews. There was, and still is, an acknowledged bias toward students with interest and proficiency in large animal medi-cine. When I decided to apply to vet school, I was strongly urged to avoid talking about my allergies, my interest in working as an exotic vet, and most critically, my vegetarianism. I eschewed eating mammals in my late teens—a form of vegetarianism Kevin brands as "not eating anything with big brown eyes."

In typical fashion, I blurted out all three facts in the first five minutes of the interview. Hiding my opinions has never been my forte. Luckily, the panel of four male vets grilling me were more interested in my colourful research history. The interview was also successful due to the fact that I had been raised to treat people "with authority" as equals—irritating in a ten-year-old, but useful in adult confrontations.

During my classes at OVC, I was confronted with many occasions where animal welfare was assigned a secondary role to animal use. When we learned about foetotomy as an alternative to expensive C-section in cows, we were taught the key anatomical zones to apply Gigli wire, a manoeuvrable saw, to remove limbs and the head of a calf. I asked whether it was convention to inject Euthansol into the calf so it wouldn't suffer. I was told in very confident tones that the foetus feels no pain before it is born. An indefensible and self-serving idea, but I suppose no different than medical doctors who argued that infant boys did not experience pain during circumcision. That is before local anaesthetic became a routine procedure.

In third-year vet school, we were trained in surgical techniques with repeated surgeries on lambs and dogs. The first two surgeries were recovery procedures where we could evaluate our success by monitoring the animals for recovery, sepsis, and pain control. The third surgery was a non-recovery euthanasia. The animals were healthy prior to the surgeries and were subjected to limb amputations, intestinal resections, and splenectomies. Students who were vehemently opposed to the surgeries were permitted exemptions provided they conduct the same surgeries on cadavers. We were cautioned to not even consider asking for exemptions if we owned leather clothing or shoes, or were not strict vegetarians.

Although I could see the value in knowing whether a surgery was successful by witnessing the recovery, and I knew that a cadaver could in no way simulate the bleeding control needed in a live surgery, I was repelled by the idea of inflicting pain and suffering on animals for no other reason than to learn a skill. To me, it seemed to be more of a way to numb any empathy for animals. Prioritizing the human client was stressed over caring for the real patient. Vets are often asked to choose the human value over animal welfare for financial or cosmetic reasons. Ear cropping, declawing, and euthanizing healthy animals when a client moves or dies are typical examples. I firmly believe that every animal has unalienable rights. In my care, the animal is always the patient. If I believed differently, I would have opted for human medicine.

We were given a presentation about the surgical options prior to committing to one of the two programs. The lecturer was a pompous, condescending anaesthesiologist who spent sixty minutes of the allotted fifty-minute time slot describing medical advances achieved through animal research. When the bell finally rang, announcing the start of our next lecture, requiring a wild five-minute dash through the corridors of the vet college, he was finally prompted to engage with us. "Any questions?" he asked. Students were scrambling to stuff books into knapsacks and move to the next classroom.

"Yes," I said. "How could you profess to make this a debate session about the merits of performing surgery on healthy animals and then just pad it with irrelevant information about lab animal research? And how could you ignore the raised hands throughout the talk and not provide any forum for discussing our concerns?"

He reddened and glared hard at me. "Ah, Ms. Seely." He smiled. "You are one of our more mature students, aren't you? How many times did it take you to get into the program?" It was a pointless barb in a small class that knew my history and marks.

I just shook my head and shrugged.

I researched options other than the two offered by the school. I found a surgery program available in Washington state where students were taught surgery on humane society dogs, performing necessary lumpectomies, neutering, and ovariohysterectomies. I spent three weeks in the company of three fellow Canadians and a group of American students who were all seeking humane alternatives to their vet schools' surgery programs. We practised sewing on oranges and leather, looking like a classroom of girls doing needlepoint in Victorian times. We were assigned dogs from the local shelter. My dog was a gentle spaniel with an intact mature uterus and ovaries, as well as a satisfying number of lumps and skin tags which I removed at the time of the spay. I neutered a further three toms, and assisted with the surgeries of my fellow students. It was a short, intense curriculum.

At the end of the program, we celebrated by going on a three-day hike. I was amazed and a little frightened to discover that several of the students were carrying small handguns. It generated a heated cross-border discussion. I announced that I didn't know anyone who owned a gun. My shocked American companions told me they didn't know anyone who didn't own a gun.

I segued from the course in Washington to more cross-border immersion as an intern at a wildlife rehabilitation centre in Florida. I worked under the relaxed supervision of a young, recently graduated veterinarian. He allowed me to stitch up injured raccoons and hand-raised skunks, wire the broken jaw of a crocodile, and pin fractured wings of blue herons and falcons. I became quite comfortable in surgery gloves with scalpels and needle drivers, and managed to not kill any of my patients.

The final summer of vet school requires that students pair up with practitioners to learn practical skills and experience real veterinary situations. I chose to work with an equine vet who had a booming practice close to Guelph. Adam was strictly a horse vet and claimed he would happily run over a farm dog or cat if it got in his path. He had a sweet setup with an indoor arena and groom on his farm. This was part of his veterinary practice. His day began with a dressage session on a horse tacked and groomed by his "vet tech". He would ride to classical music booming through the arena. He would then hand the sweaty horse to the tech at the end of the session, gather up the day's files from his wife who doubled as the office manager, and then head out on farm calls.

I accompanied him on the calls, learning that an equine practice involves hours of driving. Adam taught me the value of knowing where all the best cafés are, which stables boast the nicest bathrooms, and where to find the cheapest gas. Identifying the bathrooms was key. I started the summer with a five-month bump, the beginnings of my daughter Savannah, and ended with a good sized eight-and-a-half-month watermelon. This meant shrinking room for a full bladder. The pregnancy limited my assistance, and I became more of a note-taker and observer. Adam's wife had suffered a diaphragmatic hernia during her pregnancy when a horse butted her with his head. Adam was unsurprisingly paranoid about my condition.

I saw a huge spectrum of equine medicine, and we often worked twelve-hour days. Adam was fond of implying causation when he referred to great vets and the number of divorces they withstood. He was proudly on his third marriage.

The summer also afforded me my first introduction to equine chiropractic. Adam had learned the skill from a British chiropractor twenty years earlier. He would later go on to complete his certification when it became available, grumpily going through the motions for the dog and cat components. I saw incredible results from horse adjusting, as well as the spectrum of reactions—positive and negative—that it triggered among clients.

Although I enjoyed seeing Adam practise, it left me itchy for a more-active role. It was frustrating just watching from the sidelines with my burgeoning belly, and without a degree. I eagerly anticipated the day I could be at the helm, both in traditional medicine, and in adjusting the equine patients.

Zoo Internship

A HIGHLIGHT OF MY YEARS in vet school was a stint at the Calgary Zoo, the summer between marrying Kevin and conceiving Savannah. Because of my experience at the wildlife centre in Florida, and my Master's experience with seals, I was offered the coveted summer internship. My responsibilities included assisting the three resident veterinarians as well as the less-welcoming, but very knowledgeable, vet tech staff. The days were never routine. We handled exotic patients from the local community, injured wildlife, and monitored the health of all the resident zoo animals.

I lived in a small apartment within the zoo. It had been used to house a naive pregnant chimp prior to my arrival. When I arrived, the chimp had been rehoused to the Great Apes exhibit. One of my daily tasks was to ensure that the young chimp mother, a very reluctant mom, was success-fully nursing her infant. We would feed the mother only when her baby was attached to a nipple. She quickly caught on and the infant chimp thrived, even though he was often dangling precariously while his mom cavorted around the chimp enclosure. The young chimp mother was really just a goofy teen. Her greatest pleasure was filling her mouth with water and making faces at the tourists who would gather near the chain link fence. When a satisfying crowd had gathered, she would spit copi-ously and then dash off to a corner with an ear-to-ear grin.

For five days a week I was on call twenty-four hours. We had a menagerie of injured and orphaned wildlife which had to be fed and monitored several times daily and sometimes, through the night. I bottle-fed three orphaned moose calves, a couple of fawns, and a litter of raccoons.

A nest of young starlings was brought to the clinic with their small bodies covered in lesions that looked like the bubonic plague. Each "boil" had a small crater hole. They were the breathing tunnels for the burrowing Cuterebra larva. We had to excise them like a carefully harvested pimple, avoiding breaking the larvae as they were gently squeezed out. Some of the fledglings had more mass from the parasite than from their own bodies.

We also had a Gila monster delivered to the back door of the clinic in a large box with a note proclaiming it was found behind a dumpster at a local mall. It seemed like a baby being abandoned at the church steps, but a bit of a changeling baby. Gila monsters are large, sluggish creatures with venomous bites. It was a rather frightening moment when we opened the box. After ensuring he was healthy, and after a two-week period in quarantine, we added him to the reptile exhibit.

Days were filled with routine examinations of the reptiles, birds, and mammals at the zoo. All the animals were on a regular schedule for health checks. I assisted in blood collection and processing. My skills in venipuncture with seals gave me an edge over previous interns, and earned me the reluctant respect of the technicians who were used to a constant rotation of vet students in need of much hand holding. I required a lot of instruction in other domains though. I had to learn how to safely restrain snakes, including highly venomous ones; and how to handle small birds without injuring them, and large birds of prey without getting injured.

One day, a bag of squirrels was delivered by a couple who discovered the group in a local park, writhing on the ground and unable to move in any linear direction. They had somehow become tangled in tree sap and their tails were entwined and knotted. The resultant squirrel mass was a dangerous Gordian Knot of biting heads. I administered gas anaesthetic with a mask, moving quickly through the group as different heads groggily revived and lifted at varying intervals. One of the vets amputated necrotic pieces of tail and we slowly teased the group apart until we had nine individual squirrels with varying tail lengths. The surgery was photographed by a local paper. The following day, I appeared on a full-colour, front-page spread in the local paper. This was the same tabloid that had a bikini clad girl—the Sunshine Girl—on its back page. From then on, I was called the sunshine girl for the remainder of my internship.

The zoo had a collection of Przewalski's horses, a rare and endangered wild horse subspecies native to Central Asia. They were collaborating with other zoos to captive-breed the horses with aims of reintroducing them to Mongolia. One of the stallions was overly successful in the herd and had proudly fathered a large number of foals. The decision was made to vasectomize him in order to control the dominance of his genetics in the herd. We would still allow breeding and courtship behaviour. I had previously assisted in surgery on a lion and a ball python in the controlled environment of the zoo surgical theatre. The surgery on the stallion in an outdoor enclosure was infinitely scarier.

We corralled and isolated the stallion. He was a rearing and bucking mass of angry muscle. We darted him with a blow dart. This is a skill particular to zoo vets where a dart delivering a paralytic anaesthetic agent is blown through a pipe with a sharp breath of air. The first two bounced harmlessly off his thick hide and only ended up provoking him further. He would charge at the six-foot temporary enclosure and looked ready to jump it. The third dart satisfactorily penetrated his gluteal muscle. We nervously witnessed a few more charges before his legs buckled and he collapsed to the ground.

I was responsible for kneeling on his massive neck and holding his head down while monitoring his pupils and blink response to gauge the level of anaesthesia. Horses cannot lift themselves off the ground without employing the leverage of their big heads. If you hold their head down, you can restrain a fully conscious horse, though you wouldn't want to be caught in the tangle of thrashing legs. We had recruited a board-certified equine surgeon from the Okotoks clinic, a specialist who regularly did surgery on million-dollar race and performance horses. The surgery went quickly and smoothly with an injectable anaesthetic ensuring the stallion's immobility. The zoo vet then delivered an intravenous reversing agent, and we all ran as fast as possible to the safety of the nearby jeep. It was a bit like being party to the running of the bulls in Pamplona. We had barely closed the jeep door when the stallion staggered to his feet, tore around the corral with poorly coordinated feet, and charged out of the intentionally open gate.

I spent many of my free hours in the bird exhibit where a Moluccan umbrella cockatoo adopted me as her favourite human. It was a gorgeous tropical oasis with a glass cover and fragrant tropical plants and flowers. The birds flew freely in a lush humid microclimate. The cockatoo would fly down to meet me, gravitating to my bounty of untamed hair. On each arrival, she zeroed in on me and perched on my shoulder, purring in my ear, and grooming my cheek and hair. I fantasized about smuggling her out in a knapsack.

My other favourite spot was the elephant exhibit. It housed a group of three females, including a mother and a young calf. The baby was around eighteen months old and was cute, playful, and clumsy. It was a dangerous combination in a toddler weighing around a thousand pounds. The keepers used an elephant stick to remind her of their personal space. She would comfortably barge into them, much like a puppy does, but with much more serious ramifications. The matriarch decided that she liked me and would approach every time I arrived with the vets. She allowed me to handle her baby, an enormous compliment. During any hours where I had no scheduled chores, I would head over to the elephant exhibit. The keepers let me hang out in the enclosure, sometimes riding on the back of the enormous African female, where I was safe from the adolescent blunderings.

When I had a full weekend off, I hitchhiked to the neighbouring village of Canmore. Tracey, a friend and fellow vet student, was working at a vet clinic there. She would include me in the active weekends the town was renowned for. We mountain biked trails, hiked to alpine meadows, skinny-dipped in glacial lakes, and kept our eyes peeled for grizzly bears. We rode "bar bikes" at night to the local pubs. These were under-sized banana bikes that students picked up for less than $10 at garage sales. They could be safely left anywhere without concerns of theft.

I had one full week of vacation mid-summer. Kevin and my dad joined me for the week, when we rode horses through the foothills of the Rockies. We rode through riverbeds and past herds of wild horses. For the first two days, a thick fog descended. We could rarely see past our horses' ears as we navigated the narrow trails, wearing slick oil skins to protect us from the damp air. When the fog finally lifted on the third day, we were suddenly aware of the vast mountains around us, and of how casual we had been with cliff faces on the edges of the trails.

It was a challenging summer for me, with hours of isolation, time away from Kevin, and the claustrophobia I always experience in a city. But it was also a marvellous summer of rich experiences.

Personal Changes

KEVIN AND I STARTED OUR years in Guelph taking care of twenty-one horses used for a therapeutic riding program in exchange for free rent in an old farm house. It was not an ideal exchange. The work was considerable with all the horses requiring prompt feeding at 8 AM and 4 PM. Twenty-one stalls had to be mucked out every morning, and eighty-four hooves had to be picked clean. Initially, there were three of us sharing the chores, but the third student quit, leaving Kevin and me uniquely responsible for all the work.

The house was poorly insulated. The group in charge of the therapeutic program were very parsimonious in the allocation of funds. During the winter, the house temperature plummeted so low that a glass of water would freeze on the counter if left overnight. When we wanted to turn up the thermostat, we found a lock was placed on the door of the room where the controls were located, leaving us to shiver in an arctic house. It was not an ideal rental!

We were thus highly motivated when the option to become our own landlords arose. With the help of my dad, Kev and I bought a 1920's fixer-upper, 800-square-foot house. We rented the top half to my friend and classmate, Jiffy, and her long-term naturalist boyfriend, Chris. Kev was studying at the Canadian Memorial Chiropractic College in Toronto and would leave at 5:30 in the morning and generally return home at 10 PM. These crazy hours allowed him to avoid the stop-and-go traffic congestion of the notorious Highway 401. Our lives were not typical of the party-hungry young vet students that marked my cohort. We functioned like a married couple, nine years of living together ever since our first month of meeting at Acadia University.

I was marriage paranoid, dreading the white dressed princess-of-the-night event, as well as having fears of sliding into a humdrum relationship once the knot was tied. In our first year together, I told Kevin that marriage was not an option. Several years later, I mellowed out and said I would only marry him if he learned how to ride. I was partly motivated by my love of horses and riding, and perhaps partly to create an impossible barrier. Kevin had been tossed and trampled by a horse as a kid. He exacted the promise that I would be the one to propose if he met my stringent requirement.

In my second year of vet school, Kevin announced that he had learned how to ride. I still can't fathom how he achieved that with his short windows of time between commuting, studying, and spending time with me. But he did it! Not only did he overcome his fear, he had also learned to trot and canter. He had managed to finagle riding lessons from my other good vet-class friend, Christina.

I fulfilled my part of the bargain and proposed that night.

When we knocked on the door separating our section of the house with Jiffy's living area, we discovered a potent love bug was in the air. Jiffy and Chris had also gotten engaged that same night.

Kev and I married six weeks later, on New Year's Eve, by the Christmas tree at my parents' home. I wore a green cotton dress which cost only $39.99. Christina played the Pachelbel Canon on my dad's piano. We exchanged vows by the living room fireplace while guests held small beeswax candles that exhausted their wicks in ten minutes. We ensured the ceremony would be no longer than the candles' limit. My parents arranged for the hospital where they worked to cater the event. They had kiboshed my suggestion of having a pot luck. The food was remarkably good. No hospital jello or mashed potatoes in the offerings. We had turkey and salmon, a multitude of salads and a big banana rum cake.

Both the wedding and the marriage proved me wrong in expectations. I was not forced into acting the part of white princess for the night. It was a blast of a party with friends and family meeting, mingling, and dancing. And to date, twenty-five years of marriage with my best friend has been endlessly exciting, romantic, and never humdrum.

Around midnight in November of 1994, I woke up with the most violent bout of vomiting. Unable to sleep, I started reading Kevin's Merck Manual for differentials. By morning, Kevin and I were wondering if this could possibly be morning sickness. Kev dashed off to the pharmacy and brought home a pregnancy test kit. Indeed, I was pregnant. I stayed home that morning, alternating between toilet bowl and bed, wondering how I would ever survive months of this purging. Kev arrived home from work at noon. He, too, was in the throes of nausea. Turns out we were both victims of food poisoning.

It was a useful bug. I would never have otherwise suspected pregnancy. That morning of vomiting was the only bout of "morning sickness" that I would experience in any pregnancy. I was a bit shocked to discover I had functional female plumbing. Menarche hit me late at age sixteen and I could count on one hand the number of non pill-induced periods I had experienced. The most recent had been one month previous, the first in four years, likely triggered by a decrease in training volume following the Marine Corps marathon. I would go on to have two more periods in the next ten years while bearing three children. Pretty much every egg I laid was fertilized!

I gave birth in my last summer of vet school, after my externship placement. I had two weeks of freedom from school responsibilities and filled them with painting the house, shingling the outside, and generally nesting. I would do the same at each subsequent pregnancy, clearly as hard wired in humans as in birds. I swam every day in Guelph Lake. One swim left me stranded two kilometres from my car when the sky erupted into a thunderstorm. I walked back dripping to the car, barefoot on the isolated dirt road, ballooned with an eight-month pregnancy and luckily unwitnessed in my stretched-out, one piece Speedo.

Savannah arrived in early August of 1994 after three days of consistently timed three-minute contractions. I swam for an hour each of the first two days, timing the contractions as I treaded water. When she made her entry on day three, Kevin and I were exhausted from two days of minimal sleep. The last night had us playing cribbage all night with no sleep. The score pad was a mix of cribbage scores and contraction intervals. I believe Kevin won.

Our doctor, who was game to perform home deliveries, along with a labour coach, arrived in the early morning. Savannah would take her time before finally arriving at 8 PM. My father showed up mid-afternoon and was able to witness the birth of his first grandchild, converting a reluctant physician and worried father into a raving proponent of home births. Savannah slept in bed with us that night, nursing like a champ, and generally teaching us everything we needed to know about being first-time parents.

I took the fall semester off after delivering Savannah, the most gorgeous and good-natured baby. I wrote my veterinary boards along with my classmates in September that year, wrapped in the warm fuzz of a prolactin brain, caring minimally how I did, and rushing through the sections so I could meet Kev in the exam break and nurse from engorged breasts. I somehow passed!

I completed my last semester with the class of '96, eight months after the date emblazoned on the leather jacket most of my classmates proudly sported: "OVC Falcons Class of 95." Somehow, I was able to get though it all; pumping between surgeries, farm calls, and hauling Savannah with me to wildlife seminars and weekend rounds. Kevin took Thursdays off to enjoy one day of full-time parenting. We hired Magali, a nineteen-year-old with fluorescent multicoloured hair, nose piercings and tattoos, for four days a week. Magali would be our personal Mary Poppins. Savannah became well-known to the punk teen crowd in Guelph, and I would often hear "Hello Sav" from spiky, green-haired teens on the bus.

I graduated as the sole DVM in December 1995, seven months after my cohort graduated, and officially part of the class of '96 who would graduate as a group five months later. Kevin orchestrated a party and horse sleigh ride for my extended family in my honour. I took my grad pictures with Savannah in arms. My career as a veterinarian was officially launched.

Introduction to Chiropractic

WHILE I WAS FINISHING UP my vet degree, Kevin graduated from Chiropractic college. He joined a couple of local Guelph chiropractors as an associate. He was given the option to build his practice with Saturday hours, albeit without any reception support on weekends. I would help out as unpaid labour to find patient files and handle billing and scheduling. Savannah was another unpaid volunteer, sleeping under the desk in her car seat or nursing quietly at the front desk. She was a potent advertisement for Kevin's comfort and expertise with children, and the practice grew exponentially with young families.

Every Saturday, I witnessed chiropractic success stories and purported miracles. Patients were eager to share their stories with me about my husband with the magic hands. One patient had been suffering for over ten years with what the doctors termed, "otic hypersensitivity". She couldn't stand noise. Even the sound of her hair swishing over her ears was an irritant. She wore her hair pageboy style to avoid the irritation. Her family doctor prescribed Prozac which didn't change the noise level she experienced, but it made her "feel better about it."

After a couple weeks of adjustments, she reported that it was gone! She could even vacuum without reaction.

Kev would occasionally boast that he helped five women get pregnant in his first year in practice, with only my pregnancy achieved the conventional way.

He told one woman in her early forties that she was subluxated in the triad of areas innervating her uterus and ovaries. He recommended that she consider birth control if she was not already using some method of contraception.

She responded with anger saying she had spent much of her twenties and early thirties trying to conceive. She had come to terms with her "infertility" and her three cats and two dogs were her children. She quite resented Kev resurrecting an old hurt.

After two months with chiropractic care, she came in and punched Kev not too gently on the shoulder. "I'm pregnant," she announced. The baby would be eagerly welcomed into the world. I seem to recall the baby's being called Kevin in acknowledgment of the debt, but Kev accuses me of false memory on that detail.

I had my own tale of chiropractic success. When I entered vet school, I was sure that I would have to restrict my practice to hypoallergenic animals. I thought I'd continue my marine biology beginnings with a career as a marine mammal veterinarian. I started getting adjusted by various members of Kevin's family as I moved through the five years of the vet program. Kevin was the last of the four sons to opt to become a chiropractor; and two sisters-in-law were similarly grads of the Canadian Memorial Chiropractic College. Kevin's parents were homesteaders, back-to-the-land granolas. Kevin and his twin, Keith, were on a clear trajectory toward traditional medicine, encouraged by teachers with their high marks and an aptitude for science. Their mentor in medicine at the time was a chain-smoking French-Canadian general practitioner. When they first encountered chiropractic, they gravitated to it as a natural fit from their "granola" upbringing.

Kev's oldest brother, Sean, was an asthmatic. On one occasion, he was so incapacitated with lack of oxygen, he fell down the homestead stairs. His parents brought him to a local chiropractor. She not only resolved the back pain from the fall, but also seemed to provide huge relief from the asthma.

Sean was the first to decide to study chiropractic even though it meant returning to college to pick up the science credits he needed to apply after completing a degree in languages. Keith and Denis followed suit. Kevin was the last to apply after the detours I created in my career path which took us through Europe, a year in California, and finally Guelph. He, too, would graduate at the ripe age of thirty-one.

To return to my chiropractic transformation, all these family chiros afforded me free care, often being the guinea pig for Kevin to practise on with feedback from the practising chiropractors in the family. I soon discovered that my allergies were almost neutralized with an adjustment.

The best test was "Rowdy", a gorgeous hairy mutt who lived under the kitchen table at the Mahoney homestead. If I were adjusted during a Rowdy-induced wheeze attack, it was tantamount to taking my Ventolin inhaler, without the anxiety caused by the adrenaline it delivered.

This meant I did not have to restrict my practice to seals, dolphins, and octopuses! Although I love the challenge of exotics, I truly hate cities, and sadly, zoo medicine required the pairing of those two. I was free to pursue a traditional veterinary practice.

Animal chiropractic held obvious appeal to me, particularly after just witnessing it passively in Adam's practice during my summer externship. The regular exposure to human success stories at Kevin's office was also a big incentive to see what could be accomplished with animal patients. We had a brief introduction in my third year of the program where a lunch hour lecture was offered to discuss animal chiropractic. Our lecturer was our familiar radiology professor. He told us that in his years as an equine vet, he had been irked to lose many clients to a local chiropractor. He admitted to shadowing the chiropractor for a day in order to "learn" the techniques. He then started "adjusting" and charging clients for it. He was very disparaging about the profession, stating with great conviction that "chiropractors require minimal schooling, generally a couple of weeks."

The entire class pivoted in my direction to watch me as I raised my hand, red faced and sputtering. "The school is a four year and a half year program after a minimum of two years of undergrad, with most having an undergraduate science degree," I corrected him. "And how did your patients respond after you 'adjusted' them after learning the technique in one day?"

"Nothing happened," he retorted. "Of course, nothing happened. The whole thing is hogwash." He seemed unperturbed at admitting to collecting money for a procedure he deemed quackery.

I was not at all surprised that his sham adjustments had been unsuccessful.

In my last year of vet school, Kev's older brother, Sean, asked if we had heard about a course for veterinary chiropractic. He reported that a woman who had graduated from his Chiropractic college, Palmer College in Iowa, had started a school to train animal chiropractors. Dr. Sharon Willoughby had been an outlier in school. She was older than the typical student, having practised as a vet for twenty years before entering the four-year program. Chiropractic students are notorious at parties for palpating and adjusting each other while under the influence of a few beers. Sharon would be found in the basements at these parties, palpating reluctant cats, and adjusting dogs.

When she graduated, she opened her doors to animals uniquely and was soon busier than she could handle. She doubled her prices and was still swarmed.

She decided to start a course geared toward vets and chiropractors, to teach the art of animal adjusting. Kev and I were intrigued. We felt we were a unique combo to provide this service. We headed down to the first module in 1995. We were accompanied by seven veterinarians from the Guelph area.

As Kevin pointed out in the group introduction, "These guys must all have an awesome chiropractor." They were all patients of Kev's.

One couple in particular were good friends and avowed large animal vets. Don was a cow vet completing a post-secondary degree at Guelph. He had met his soon-to-be wife there, Sybil, a German vet pursuing post-grad specialization in equine medicine. When Don was first adjusted by Kevin, he described the experience as almost orgasmic.

The first module was the cervical region of the spine. I was fresh from my vet degree with hubris about my palpating skills which could detect increased size of a liver, kidney irregular margins, and an ovarian follicle.

When I first palpated the neck of the patient horses we were working with, I felt nothing. I couldn't differentiate the bones let alone assess whether they were moving smoothly. Chiropractors were better equipped at spinal palpation but less versed in animal anatomy. One chiropractor tried to locate the horse's spine in the nuchal ligament, the large elastic structure above the vertebral column which helps support the horse's heavy skull. The cervical spine in a horse is not housed along its top line, but is rather buried much lower in the middle half of the neck.

We returned from the course enthusiastic about adjusting animal patients. We had five more modules to complete but were urged to prac-tise our cervical techniques in the interim. Kevin and I were taking riding lessons in Guelph at the time. Kevin was honing his newfound skills past the introductory walk and trot, and was learning to canter and jump. We started adjusting the school horses for free. Even though our skill set was pretty green, horses improved so dramatically that the beginner horses Kev had been assigned were being promoted to advance lessons, as they could jump comfortably again. We also saw occasional canine patients. Unfortunately, the first dog Kevin adjusted tried to bite his hand off. Ironically, the dog did brilliantly, a drooling mastiff who never drooled again after the first adjustment. Much to Kevin's horror, a dog I adjusted at his clinic left me with a flea migrating over my cheek. He concluded that he would rather restrict his practice to cleaner, more bite-inhibited humans.

Setting Up in The Valley

WITH A BOOMING HUMAN CHIROPRACTIC practice and a new baby, we elected to do the least clever thing in the spring of 1996 and move. We left the house we owned in Guelph and packed our lives into a U-Haul and headed up to the Ottawa Valley. The house wouldn't sell for another twelve months, leaving us saddled with a mortgage, a monthly rental cost, and pretty much no income.

We had decided to leave Southern Ontario for the greener pastures of the Ottawa Valley where we had Kevin's twin, Keith, and my parents within an hour's drive. Southern Ontario had always felt a bit alien to my Quebec roots. We liked the idea of being able to school our kids in French, as well as being closer to cousins and grandparents. I was violently against living in a town or city. I morph into an ugly Mr. Hyde when I'm forced to spend any time with neighbours close enough to witness my night clothing choices, or lack thereof. Despite being a Montreal product, I had left cities behind when I was old enough to choose my own path and had headed out to the Maritimes for undergrad schooling. It took around two months of beings immersed in maritime small-town friendliness to thaw the big Montreal paranoid ice chip on my shoulder. Every so often, I could see hints of that paranoid claustrophobia emerge in Guelph. I had spent childhood summers at an island cottage on a lake in the Laurentian Hills, wondering why adults would choose to weekend in Paradise, and spend weekdays in Purgatory. I was determined to choose

Paradise for three hundred and sixty-five days a year.

We had scouted the realty near Pembroke and decided to rent a two-bedroom rustic bungalow on Lake Doré while researching our options for a permanent house on the water. We bought a building in town for Kevin to start a chiropractic practice. I found a job as an associate veterinarian in a rural practice in Cobden. After two weeks of travelling with the clinic owner, Paul, I was given the keys to a truck, a mobile kit of surgical instruments and drugs, and complete autonomy to do farm calls. I listened exclusively to the local country radio, wore blue coveralls and boots, and smelled like cow shit for the year of playing at being James Herriot.

I had a pager which was a permanent fixture on my person. I was slave to its annoying buzz for eight out of every fourteen days. I still experience an increase in heart rate when I hear the shrill alarm of french fries being ready at fast food restaurants. I suspect it triggers the same visceral reaction in Savannah. I would often pick her up at the daycare after a ten-hour shift, get home and start supper preparations with Kevin, and then the little black box would start vibrating and beeping. I would have to head out immediately for a farm call, peeling Savannah off my legs like a limpet, and usually not return until she was asleep.

I was trusted as the expert in all my virgin forays into surgeries which I had only studied and could get meagre advice from notes with high-lighted sections and hand-drawn facsimiles of diagrams which had briefly been drawn on blackboards. There was no YouTube or Internet then. I performed my first Caesarean section on a cow in the pouring rain with a taciturn farmer holding an umbrella over the incision with the edges of the umbrella delivering a steady stream of water down my neck as I sewed. I did another by the headlights of my truck in sub-zero temperatures, glad to immerse my gloved hands into the warm viscera of the cow as I sutured her uterus after delivering a healthy but oversized calf.

I discovered that a cow can expel her vagina like an inverted sock when she strains after calving. The mass of tissue, often dragged through mud and faeces, had to be hosed clean before being squished back into place. A well-placed epidural aimed to prevent it from being ejected again, occasionally failed to do so. I would push the uterus into place and promptly have the cow strain and push it out again, usually delivering an explosion of faeces and urine right into my face.

In contrast, the small animal clinic was a welcome sanctuary of cleanliness. I enjoyed the controlled environment—and the assistance of a lab technician—to do the surgeries there. I became adept at the bread-and-butter surgeries of vet practice, rotating between two tables as I spayed and neutered cats and dogs, just changing sterile gloves in between. I would often perform six or seven surgeries before lunch.

Vets are required to be jacks-of-all-trades of every hospital department. I held wriggly dogs while wearing a lead gown for radiographs, and would strip off the twelve-pound apron to disappear into a dark room to hand dip and develop the X-rays. I would dispense advice on aggressive or destructive dogs. I could slide a needle into a cat's bladder, and then pore over a microscope to evaluate whether there was evidence of infection. I would patiently count the number of different blood cell types with a hand clicker to gauge the health of a patient. In 1995, vet practice in rural Canada likely resembled the workday of a GP at the turn of the century.

I continued the training schedule to become an animal chiropractor, using my allotted vacation time to fly to Illinois to complete the modules detailing thoracic, lumbar, sacro-pelvic, and extremity adjusting. I weaned Savannah at age two during one of these modules—leaving Kevin to console her in this forced independence. Three months later, I flew down again for the final integrated module and exams.

The group had become a cohesive class as we returned to each module, and I had befriended a number of veterinarians and chiropractors who would graduate with my cohort. We would often trade adjustments.

"Would you mind checking out the innervation of my ovaries and uterus?" I asked one of the instructor chiropractors whose techniques and skill I respected. "I seem to be at a standstill ever since I weaned my daughter and I've only had one period since."

He checked me and said, "Everything seems fine to me. In fact, your uterus is thrumming with energy."

When I flew home, both Kevin and Keith were convinced I looked different and Keith picked up a pregnancy test at a 24-hour pharmacy. It was positive!

I continued to work in mixed practice until I had swollen to a six-month balloon. At the six-month mark, I was called to a calving at a farm in Beachburg. It was 2 AM and the cow was in distress. The uterus had twisted and the calf was trapped. When I incised through the abdomen wall and freed the calf, I was told the farmer couldn't help me as he had suffered a heart attack recently. His son likewise couldn't help because he had a bad back. I had to wrestle with the weight of a large calf and work on getting him breathing with a belly protruding to such a degree that I had a hard time getting my arm inside the abdomen to free him from the twisted mess. I completely ignored the request to do the surgery without anaesthetic as they were likely going to slaughter the cow and didn't want to taint the meat. It was a surgery to herald the end of my mixed-animal career, already a huge stretch for a vegetarian, bleeding heart, and animal lobbyist. I resuscitated the calf and then sutured the cow's abdomen hoping she would be allowed to convalesce and survive. I suspect she was more likely meat for the farmer's table later that week, despite the doses of painkiller and antibiotics I had given her.

That farm call both ended my large animal career and marked the beginning of the next phase of our lives. I drove home as the sun slowly dawned that morning, shaky and tired, and I crested a hill on a road I had never before travelled. There was a For Sale sign at the top of the hill. I had just passed a small lake and wondered if the land bordered on it. I parked on the shoulder of the road and climbed awkwardly over the fence. I worried briefly about being seen. I was in coveralls coated liberally in blood. My face was blood spattered. I could reasonably be mistaken for a Charles Manson follower after a midnight slaughter.

The driveway was devoid of cars and the house looked empty. I scanned the view from the porch—an unspoiled open vista of a quiet lake, with no houses in sight—as the sun turned the sky to cotton candy pink and blue.

Kev and I submitted our offer that morning. After some mild haggling, it was accepted two days later. We had been searching for eight months, and the property had been listed for three years. The house was unprepossessing. It had been used as a hunt-camp for six couples and bore the neglect of too many indifferent owners. But the land and lake were magnificent, a hundred and fifty-six acres of mixed forest with two private lakes. The price would buy a small apartment in Toronto at the time. We would have paid anything they asked. It was perfect.

The Beginnings of Animal Chiropractic Practice

I DABBLED IN ANIMAL CHIROPRACTIC that first year in practice. I was working over sixty hours a week and on salary, so there wasn't much opportunity to offer chiropractic services. Paul would sometimes send me on a farm call where there was a particularly ornery horse and recommend that I adjust the horse first before vaccinating or examining the patient. He had witnessed horses becoming docile after being adjusted. Although he was hard put to explain it, he was game to capitalize on its apparent effects. I would feel guilty though. I would adjust the horse, usually an atlas subluxation, the first cervical vertebrae. In humans, a misaligned atlas often results in migraines or a headache. I could only guess the horses were suffering from the same. When I adjusted them, they would visibly relax and lower their head and drop their bottom lip. Then I would whisk out a vaccine needle and jab them in the neck. It felt like a bit of a betrayal.

One dog I saw at the clinic had a seemingly miraculous cure from his pain from splenic cancer. The cancer was advancing, and my ministrations wouldn't change that, but the owner, a seventy-year-old widower was vested in keeping his dog pain free and alive as long as possible. A television network heard about the story and filmed me adjusting the dog in a rather saccharine Christmas season special.

They continued filming as I drove down dark snow-covered country lanes to a barn where I was to see a horse for the first time. The owner described how the gelding, Rufus, wouldn't run with his tail up, and seemed grumpy when he was ridden.

I said, "Hmm. The tail sounds like a sacral issue."

I gently raised the tail and Rufus's legs buckled and he almost collapsed on top of the filming crew.

There was a mad scramble as the crew, almost exclusively consisting of well-dressed city people, rearranged themselves into safer viewing vantage points.

I adjusted the sacrum which gave a rare but audible pop. I positioned myself to raise the tail again, but it was already rising and swishing from side to side. Rufus turned and nuzzled my shoulder with apparent gratitude. In the final Christmas special, he was personified in that moment as thanking me for making this his best Christmas ever.

I would continually garner media attention with animal chiropractic. In rural Canada, it probably had a ring of weird California extremism. The tone was always positive with clients allowed to gush about the improvements in their pets' conditions. It was a marked contrast to the negative media attention human chiropractic would attract. In the same time frame that my Christmas special aired, a segment about human chiropractic would focus on a child with a spinal tumour being adjusted. Although the adjustment had no positive or negative impact on the child's outcome, the camera would loiter on the boy navigating awkwardly on his hands and knees as if rendered paralyzed by an adjustment. Kevin would have to reassure patients after each media attack, as well as accept a brief drop in new patients. For some reason, fear, fanned by the media reports of human chiropractic, never seemed to dissuade people from seeking care for their pets.

My stint as a mixed-animal vet came to an end when the anticipated arrival of my second child coincided with the end of my year's contract with Paul. I had been madly painting rooms, emptying boxes, and generally nesting in the house on the lake. We had moved to the house one month before the due date. The hunt camp had been morphed into a home and we were delighted to discover that the thawed lake was deep, clean, and a wonderful swimming venue. I had two weeks of relative calm before the due date.

I went into labour at midnight on June 5. I laboured comfortably in a Canadian Tire inflatable kiddy pool filled with lukewarm water. My mother arrived and held Savannah. It would be my mother's first exposure to a home birth. I reassured Allison, our Ottawa midwife, that she could drive relaxedly as Savannah had been the product of three days of steady labour. Luckily, Allison had heard equally erroneous confident assertions before. She jumped into her car and arrived fifteen minutes before Forest arrived, a bare three hours after my first contraction. This would be predictive of a character who defied doing things in any prescribed way.

Forest yelled at birth like the proverbial healthy newborn. He also resisted nursing with his head turned to the left. Kevin palpated his neck and found resistance in the cervical vertebrae. To the amazement of the midwife, Kev adjusted Forest's neck around twenty minutes after he was born. A gentle pop and he settled comfortably to nurse on either side.

I started to offer chiropractic services immediately after my contract with Paul expired. I had built up a fair reputation before leaving his practice, and the phone was ringing steadily. I strapped Forest into a car seat, instructed Savannah to watch his level of sleepiness while leafing through a picture book, and would adjust horses beside the car with the windows open to monitor everything. The kids learned to be comfortable with horses early on. They also developed antipathy for the cold, smelly nature of barns. Veterinary medicine has never tempted any of them.

In those early days of practice, I had not developed an instinct for how often to adjust my patients. When I first prescribed the human schedule, and would check them twice in a week, there would generally be nothing to adjust.

My brother-in-law Sean summed it up by saying, "Your patients do better than ours. No mortgages. No driving. No sitting to watch TV."

At first, I just resorted to adjusting the patient and asking the owners to call me when they needed me again. This was crappy patient care as well as poor practice management. I eventually learned that dogs tend to hold their first adjustment for around a week, and horses for closer to one month. Cats are the best spinal patients and sometimes need only one adjustment. Kev would often remind his human patients that if they did yoga, they could see him far more infrequently. I figure that cats are the most natural of yoga practitioners.

When owners didn't call back, I assumed the adjustment had not helped. I would be far too insecure to call back and have that confirmed. One horse I saw in my first year illustrated that clearly for me. I was called to a farm deep in the back woods of the Ottawa Valley. I parked the car as close as I could safely venture, and then donned boots to walk through spring puddles and mud to get to the shelter where the horse was hibernating from the rain. The owners were a young family with two children underfoot, and one older preteen. They explained they had purchased the horse for their twelve-year-old daughter, but that the horse had become completely unrideable after the first summer.

"Did anything happen to her?" I asked? "Any falls? Trauma?"

They looked embarrassed.

"She did have a sort of funny incident last fall," the mother confessed.

She went on to explain that her daughter had run into the house briefly while tacking up the horse. She had tied the horse to a swing set. When she emerged, the horse had gone. She was found several kilometres away. The swing set was found part way down the road, at least five hundred metres away, a mangled metal mess. The swing set had been a cheap aluminum contraption. The mare had understandably spooked when the wind or her movements started the swing in action, and she had bolted with the swing set clattering in her wake.

The poor mare could hardly be palpated. Her atlas was jammed against the occiput on one side, and the muscles around it were fibrosed and scarred. I normally tease movement gently out of a stuck atlas. There was no teasing this one. I finally stood on my stool in front of the mare and gave a huge thrust, ignoring her white eyes and prancing. There was a big *thunk*, and the kids looked terrified that I had broken their horse. The mare yawned and lowered her head and let me adjust the rest of her spine without any resistance. I collected the money for the treatment, but looked back worriedly at the mare who looked asleep on her feet when I left.

I called once later that week, not to book a recheck, but just to confirm that she was OK. When voice mail answered, I asked them to call if they had any concerns. I hoped no call was good news. I was not eager to return. The mare had been so difficult to approach, I had been scared for my safety. And the long swampy trek was a good deterrent, too.

Three years later, I would get a call for a barn looking for an animal chiropractor for their school horses. They told me I had been very highly recommended. They mentioned the name of the reference, but I couldn't place it. They then told me that I had reputedly cured a crazy horse with one adjustment after she had been injured by a swing set. The mare had gone on to place at the local fair, garnering fair attention as a calm, skilled jumper, and had been sold at great profit to an eventing barn in Ottawa.

Sometimes one adjustment can do the trick. Generally, though, I would return one or two months later to check and/or adjust whatever slips, slides, riding, or age was doing to misalign my patients' spines. Clients in the horse world are a chatty and tight community. My practice started to grow exponentially.

Horse and Rider

I BLEW ON MY STIFF blue fingers and shook the pen to tease out some ink. I was once again in a cold arena checking the spines of around twelve horses. I was offering a clinic with ten confirmed horses, but typically a couple spectators would become enthusiastic as they watched from the sidelines and my numbers would increase. I looked over at the glassed-in observation room resentfully. I knew Kevin was in there in rolled-up sleeves, heater merrily plugged in, a box of Tim Hortons donuts on the coffee table.

Kevin and I had been invited to give a horse and rider seminar. We had started offering these clinics while building our practices. They were proving to be very popular. We offered a hands-on clinic where owners and horses would have their spines assessed. I would adjust the horses, and Kev would offer a discounted first visit at his clinic where OHIP insurance could be processed, waivers signed, and radiographs taken if warranted. We would start with a talk about the role of spinal health, and a review on how human and horses' backs get subluxated (which means, move aberrantly). It was a great venue for the style of communication Kevin and I had honed over our twelve years together. I would finish Kevin's sentences, tease him, and he would contradict me, and generally keep the audience entertained with our repartee.

Kevin would bring his portable chiropractic table into a tack room or office and assess the spines of riders and let them know where and if they had areas of concern. I would set up a stool in the arena and watch the horses at walk, then palpate their spines and adjust them. People are often sceptical that I can adjust an animal that is so much bigger than I am. I explain that I adjust just one bone at a time. I reassure them that my hundred and thirty-five pounds is considerably bigger than two adjacent equine vertebrae, which is all I am adjusting at one particular moment.

We started to see a trend as we relayed our findings to the clients.

"Well, that's cool," one rider remarked. "Silver and I both have left posterior ilium."

Another would interject, "Jack and I seem to both have a right anterior sacrum."

The similarities were more than coincidence. It was sometimes hard to discern whether the horse would throw the rider's back out of alignment, or if the owner was to blame for the paired imbalance. If a horse has a high hip, the rider has to modify his or her position to stay balanced. Likewise, if a rider is heavier on one stirrup, the horse has to compensate. People were often tempted to correlate their neck findings, but I never saw any consistent pattern other than coincidence explaining similarities there.

At one high level jumping stable, I adjusted twelve horses and found ten of them to sport a left posterior ilium, or high left hip.

"Who is riding all these horses?" I asked.

The owner's daughter confessed that she was the only rider.

I advised her to get adjusted. "It's much cheaper for you to get adjusted, than for me to return monthly and adjust all the horses you are throwing out of alignment."

Usually the owners would recognize the correlation. They would comment that the stirrups never felt even for them, or that the saddle always seemed to slide to one side.

The seminars grew in popularity and we were invited to stables one or two hours away. I was resigned to the mobile nature of an equine practice.

Kevin was less enthused about assessing patients miles from his practice, where he could not provide any continued care. I started pairing up with local chiropractors to offer the seminars. My practice continued to grow this way, moving into zones I would never normally acquiesce to, two to three hours from home. To keep the driving sane, I started to build a schedule of clustering stables geographically. I would see ten to twelve stables in a day, often leaving home before 6 AM and returning after dark. I restricted these insane days to once a week.

Kev and I opted for four long workdays with weekends off, and one day individually at home to parent Savannah and Forest. We hired Shirley, a local grandmother, an antithesis to our Guelph, teen-aged, purple-haired nanny. She took care of the kids on the three days we were both working.

I started back in regular vet practice at a local small animal clinic. I kept the animal chiropractic side separate, and offered both allopathic and alternative medicine at the same clinic. It sometimes made for conflicts. I knew I could resolve a chronic ear infection with an adjustment when the owner would be anticipating a renewed prescription of antibiotics. I had a hard time recommending chiropractic because of the implied self-interest.

Luckily, the staff started seeing the results of adjustments and would step in to suggest a chiropractic assessment when it was clearly warranted. I had no such conflict when a young cat was brought in for euthanasia because he could no longer do stairs.

"We are heartbroken about losing Wooley," the middle-aged woman protested. She was accompanied by her husband and three teens. The youngest was alternately crying and glaring at her parents.

"It's not just stairs he won't do," the husband added. "He can't get into the litter box so leaves us little presents all around the box."

"He likes to sleep with us, but can't climb the stairs. His life is pretty miserable."

I was patting the cat as we chatted. The sacrum was almost visibly subluxated with the tail askew to the left and a grumpy reaction whenever my hands strayed behind the rib cage.

"Would you be willing to try one sort of far-out treatment?" I ventured. "I think Wooley is just sore, and can't jump. You see how uncomfortable he is here?"

My hands almost instinctively adjusted him as I palpated. Wooley was straining to leap away, and then went almost limp on the table. Oops. Now I had to gain permission to adjust when I had just adjusted him. I offered to adjust for free since they had already paid the requisite examination fee that is required before a euthanasia.

I left the family to confer. I was counting on the kids weighting the decision. I was going to refuse to euthanize, and was hoping to avoid the showdown if they continued to demand it. Luckily, the tears won out.

"OK." The dad was the elected spokesperson. "Go ahead and crack his bones or whatever it is you do. But if it doesn't work, you have to put him to sleep next week. I refuse to sleep in a house full of cat shit and piss."

I finished the adjustments. The cat was a compliant rag doll after the key sacral area had been adjusted.

The whole family looked sceptical when I finished. There is rarely big audible releases or huge movements with small animals. I'm sure it looks like a sleight of hand, particularly for the unconvinced.

I groaned when I saw Wooley's name on the schedule the following week.

The husband was not present this time, but the wife and two of the kids were there. No tears this time. I was hopeful when all their expressions were a cheery contrast to the week before.

"We are pretty pissed off at you," the mother announced, dashing my optimism. She didn't let me suffer too long. "You are a miracle worker!" She continued, "We never used to worry about leaving food on the counters. Well. That has changed. Wooley ate all the butter out of the butter dish. And stole some toast! He can not only do stairs now, but he can get on the friggin' table and counter, too! Crazy! Can you adjust me? I'm getting kind of sore and slow, too, you know."

My heart slowed to normal and I laughed and suggested they cross the street and set up an appointment with Kevin as he was much better with two-legged patients. I think I only saw Wooley once more. He was a one-time cure.

The Wild West in Renfrew County

I SCOWLED AT THE HASTILY scrawled note by the phone. Our babysitter, Shirley, was prone to leaving telephone messages on roughly torn pieces of loose-leaf paper. With a house littered with Savannah's drawings and a fire which was constantly fed by scrap paper, notes were at high risk of being destroyed before being read.

"When did these people call?" I asked Shirley.

The note read, *Absolute emergency. Horse can't move. Foymount area. Call Bert.*

Shirley reassured me that they had just called that morning while I was at the clinic. I established that she wouldn't mind staying late, and dialled the number.

Bert was hard to understand. He again said it was an absolute emergency, and that it was a chiropractic case, not regular medicine. "Yeah, yeah, I did call my vet. He says call you!"

I shed my clinic dress pants and threw on jeans and an old sweatshirt. He told me the horse was in a distant field and was frozen in place. I pulled on my big boots and an old bulky jacket.

I was still fairly new to the area. "Where is Foymount?" I asked Shirley, a long-term resident of The Valley.

"Glory. It's at least an hour from here. Probably longer with all the snow. Some odd folk," she added ominously. "And there are drug dealers."

I headed out reluctantly. A two- or three-hour drive, and what threatened to be a horse with a broken leg, was not going to be a thankful call, and the call fee I had quoted on the phone would hardly cover my gas costs.

I stopped the car several times to consult my map. I found the farm by Bert's rough description of "The third farm with a red door, three to four miles after the intersection with a large church but no name on the road." It was years before GPS and the reigning assumption of farmers was that "Turn right at Kelly's Corners" or "If you see Don's silo, you've gone too far" were useful directions to a non-local vet.

Bert greeted me at the car. He was a bear of a man, his shaggy beard fringed with frosty spittle betraying that he had been outside for hours.

"'Bout time," he said. "Come now. The silly bugger's going to half freeze, he hasn't moved in that long."

We trudged through deep snow for five hundred metres or so, climbing over a stile to reach a windswept field. My patient stood at the top of a hill. I assumed he looked so huge because of the vantage. Once we drew near, I realized that there was no distortion from the hill. The gelding was a Belgian draft horse, and he was seriously huge.

"Wow!" I exclaimed. "What is he? Nineteen? Twenty hands?"

"A good twenty, I'd say," affirmed Bert proudly.

Hands is an archaic measurement for horse height, measured by the width of four fingers, at the point of the withers just behind the neck. Twenty hands is just over six and a half feet tall. And the horse's head towers above that point.

I laughed and held up the folding stool I had gamely carried all the way from the car. Bert and I grinned simultaneously. The stool would be useless.

"Do you have a ladder?" I asked, only half jesting. I would need to get above the horse's back to get some leverage as well as just to palpate.

"I have a better idea." Bert wandered away, leaving me with the enormous gelding.

I ran my hands over the gelding's side and rubbed his nose. He seemed remarkably calm for this supposed emergency. His back was covered in snow and his feet were partly buried, supporting the idea that he had not moved for hours. There was no evidence of any horse prints leading up to his position on the hill.

One hip was decidedly higher than the other, even with all four legs firmly planted. I palpated the stifle joint. The knees of horses are just as complicated and vulnerable to injury as those of people. One common reason for horses to be reluctant to move is a luxated patella, where the kneecap shifts laterally. The gentle giant let me feel around his knee with no resentment. The patella was in place. I felt the femur and cannon bones on his back legs. No fractures could be found and I breathed easier.

The sound of a loud motor disturbed my exam.

I turned to see Bert approaching with a huge tractor with big chain-covered tires. He pulled up beside the horse. Bert climbed out and patted the horse on his big forehead. "Good old Duke," he said, producing my patient's name. "Nothing ever riles him up."

I clambered up onto the front loader of the tractor which positioned me perfectly above Duke's back. I located and adjusted three mal-positioned vertebrae in his lumbar vertebrae. I then leaned out as far as possible over the locked and high sacroiliac joint and dropped with all my weight onto the tuber sacrale. It moved, and the gluteal muscle started to twitch. I thrust at the base of the sacrum while pulling on Duke's tail to lever the apex of the sacrum. This adjustment sounded with a loud crack which carried audibly over the snowy field.

Duke shifted weight to his left back leg, and then lunged forward, breaking though the ice which had surrounded his feet. He took a couple awkward steps, shook himself vigorously, and then trotted off.

I climbed down from the bucket.

Bert tipped his head to me and said, "Jaysus. You'd have to see it to believe it. I thought you'd broke his leg there with that crack." He climbed into the cab of the tractor and said, "Hop in. Might as well drive back. Bit warmer in here."

We drove back to a farmhouse where I was ushered inside for coffee and cookies by the fire. I was happy to thaw my fingers to write out the invoice, and happy to accept a cup of instant coffee and store-bought cookies that Bert's wife produced.

The door suddenly swung open and a teenager burst in. Ignoring me, she charged up to her parents saying "Well, she dit it! It turns out, Jenny's ma did kill her pa."

"Well, she said she would, and she did! That crazy Cherylle. Poor old Scott."

I could hear the banjo twang of the Beverly Hillbillies in my head as I hastily took my leave with images of a long-gun-toting Polish Amazon woman stalking the hills in my mind.

I read about the case in the paper the following week. A woman had been detained and questioned about killing her ex-husband by lacing his wine with antifreeze. She was ultimately convicted of that murder then tried for killing her lesbian lover. Not a trigger-happy mountain lady, but an equally crazy story. It fed into Shirley's cautions about the area. I was happy when Bert called to cancel the recheck visit. He declared that Duke was a hundred percent and back to work hauling trees out of the bush.

The German Connection

I CONTINUED TO OFFER REGULAR medicine alongside chiropractic care for many years. Don and Sybil, who started the course with Kev and me, were much more brave.

"We are going to go uniquely chiropractic," they announced through the static of a transatlantic phone call. Don, our cow vet friend from Nova Scotia, had completely fallen for Sybil, the German intern who'd come to Canada to hone her equine medicine skills. They returned to Germany to marry and set up practices there. Don survived a year with his smile and his skill carrying him through the language barrier. Nova Scotians are unilingual with their own brand of English, and are not renowned for language acquisition. Don was no exception.

After Kevin had introduced them to the joys of being adjusted, they had taken the modules in quick succession and became certified animal chiropractors. They offered this service in Germany, but were stymied in finding the time to be effective while being employed in allopathic clinics. So they quit their positions as veterinary employees and elected to offer their chiropractic services exclusively.

The stakes were high. They had just given birth to their first daughter and had no back-up plan. They invited us to Germany to stage some of the horse and rider clinics we had developed in the Valley. They were hopeful this would provide them with momentum for their new practice.

I was pregnant with my third child. The pregnancy had not been heralded by a period. I had only just weaned Forest before discovering that number three was en route. It made for much guesswork in terms of due date and we flew to Germany somewhere in my fourth or fifth month.

It was a busman's holiday. We visited four different stables with Don, Sybil and I checking the horses while Kevin examined the humans.

Germans are a different breed than Canadians. Kevin would generally get some reluctant volunteers in Canada who would eventually imbue the others with their bravery to be checked. In contrast, Germans were pulling off their shirts and queuing competitively to get on Kev's makeshift table.

They weren't happy to merely be palpated. "Crack me, *bitte!*" they demanded.

The women in Germany are not constrained by North American puritanical modesty. Shirts would fly off and all variety of bras would be comfortably displayed. It was a refreshing change, and I revelled in the kids' being immersed in a saner culture. Not long before our flight, a friend of Savannah's inspired her to copy her change style in the women's room of our local pool. The two girls would sequester themselves in the tiny space of a metal locker to don their bathing suits, hair precariously entwined in the coat hooks while perched on muddy metal floors. We went to some public swim houses in Germany and the contrast was dramatic. Men and women would freely stroll through the family change rooms naked, and the showers and saunas were similarly casual. Happily, Savannah never reverted to shyness when we returned.

The seminars were eagerly attended. Sybil acted as the translator when we did group talks.

On occasion, the group fractured into a two-ring circus. A friend of Sybil was commissioned to translate. Kev delivered ten-minute discourses on the causes of subluxations, the history of chiropractic, and our mission statement in checking both horses and riders. Franz, the translator, would summarize in very few words each time.

Everyone laughed at one point when he nodded sagely at the end of a long, complicated explanation about spinal mechanics and proclaimed "*Ja, wie er sagte,*" which roughly translated as, "Yes, as he said."

Our evenings were never quiet. We would either play endless games of *Risk* with Don and Sybil, or host their stream of friends, who would arrive, ostensibly just to visit, only to casually mention they were desperate to be checked and adjusted by the Canadian chiropractor. There was no culture of chiropractic in the country. Alternative and naturopathic medicine had a huge following, as did a practice of "bone setting". There were no chiropractic colleges on the continent, and some countries had made the practice illegal.

There was no respite from all the adjusting. Kevin is always gracious about working on holidays, and hates seeing people who need adjustments going without. But as a result, Kevin returned from the trip exhausted, and my subsequent trips were made alone.

The seminars launched the practice for Don and Sybil. They were soon busier than they could accommodate, and needed to hire associates. Their geographic range dwarfed mine as they were soon taking on clients in Denmark, Iceland, and Norway. They recognized a huge need in Europe and founded both a school for animal chiropractic and an international body to govern it.

I returned twice to assist in teaching their modules and participate in seminars for experienced animal chiropractors.

On one occasion, we offered to check horses who had been proven to be challenging for local practitioners. We were assigned to groups of four. My group boasted over forty-five years of cumulative experience; I contributed twelve of those years at that time. We were a diverse group, with practitioners from Israel, Germany, Spain, and myself, the Canadian. We palpated the horse from head to toe and wrote down our findings. There was remarkable consistency. Other than two of us finding listings in the carpal bones, and two not noting them, all other listings were identical.

It reminded me of the tutorial sessions my sister-in-law, Andrea, would set up for Kevin and another sister-in-law, Cathy, when they were both in third-year chiropractic college.

Andrea was long graduated and would palpate my back but not adjust it. "OK, Kev, what are you finding in her neck?" she would quiz. "Don't adjust. Let's see if Cathy will find the same listing?"

Both occasions were reassuring affirmations of the real and reproducible nature of the subluxations.

The German school offered a rigorous program with dissections of the pertinent anatomy and excellent lectures and presentations. There were often more than twenty countries represented among students and instructors. A large number of vets opted to uniquely offer chiropractic treatments, eschewing their years of allopathic medicine. Germany was reflecting the change, too, in the ten years since I had first visited. It was becoming increasingly rare to find a high-level competitive horse who wasn't under chiropractic care.

My German was rudimentary, embarrassingly so. The courses were taught in English, but the school was situated in Sittensen, a rural community where very little English was spoken. I dabbled with Rosetta Stone, and then painstakingly worked my way through German Duolingo. I immersed myself in German movies before my last trip. Unfortunately, there is a propensity for Nazi history movies in the Netflix German language options.

When I landed in Munich to transfer to Hamburg, I had sufficient German to translate the sign offering showers. My subsequent interview with the unsmiling, uniformed customs agent had me fully in WWII paranoia. Generally, the people I have met in Germany have done a good job at allaying any post-war bigotry. Sybil, in particular, is a kindred soul with a huge heart.

On my last visit, I had two extra hours to spare at the Hamburg airport. I saw a Desigual store, a brand my sister introduced me to. The prices were generally far too steep, but they had a bin of discount sweaters. I approached the sales lady who was completely monolingual.

"*Hast du kleine? Danke. Und ich kein benutzen eine tasche, aber schere würd gut sein.*" That roughly translates as an awkward, "Do you small? And I need no bag. But scissors would great be."

I cut off the tag and put the sweater in my carry-on bag. It felt like a treat for passing a German language test.

Shifting to Just Chiropractic

I RETURNED FROM THAT FIRST trip to Germany with renewed enthusiasm for animal chiropractic, and began to entertain the idea of limiting my traditional medicine hours. I added an afternoon a week in Ottawa to accommodate the number of patients I had attracted there. I had outgrown one clinic in Stittsville and was operating out of a kennel in the last stages of my third pregnancy. Donna and her mother Joanne had a thriving breeding kennel of English cocker spaniels. They were delighted to host clinics at their house where dog trivia and valuable training and health tips were traded along with coffee and potluck treats. It was a great venue for the erratic energy bursts and lulls of the last phase of my pregnancy.

With no menstrual cycle to mark the transition from nursing Forest to being pregnant again, I had no idea when this kid would emerge. With a body seasoned by two previous pregnancies, all my symptoms seemed to come early. I am a staunch atheist, but vulnerable to a ridiculous level of superstition. Sav had arrived on the eighth of the eighth month and Forest was born on June 6th. I fully expected to go into labour on March 3rd. My mother-in-law, Jane, arrived for the week to help in my inevitable nesting and we papered and painted a bathroom. I dutifully started with the anticipated contractions on the third. Jane and I were equally excited. It would be the first birth Jane would ever witness, having been completely knocked out with scopolamine for her three births resulting in four sons in the '60s.

But we were thwarted. I had another three weeks of erratic and prolonged contractions before giving birth. I adjusted eight horses the day before, hoping to stimulate some sort of action. Logan arrived in the calm fashion that would be completely predictive of his sunny but totally self-directed personality. The birth was very social, witnessed by both my parents, Savannah, and Forest, as well as a midwifery student. It was a relaxed copy of Forest's birth. Allison, the midwife who had presided at Forest's birth, arrived in good time for the delivery. Logan was born in the same Canadian Tire kiddy wading pool, which had been freshly cleaned and filled for the water birth.

Logan was a very tractable baby and I hauled him around to stables with me when he was at the easy stage where he would comfortably sleep whenever he was strapped into a car seat. He became a fixture at Donna's, the owner of the kennel where I adjusted dogs in Ottawa. Logan was complacently passed from arms to arms of adoring owners all morning long as I adjusted their pets. When he was around six months old, I reluctantly left him with our caregiver, Shirley, along with Forest and Savannah, and started ramping up my availability for chiropractic appointments. The number of patients was straining the capacity at the kennel. I was invited to operate my practice out of a growing veterinary clinic in Stittsville.

The owner of the practice was an engaging and energetic veterinarian, Marc, who had graduated four years before me. He had three children of almost identical ages to mine and a humour and style that was completely reminiscent of my younger brother, Andrew. He invited me to see patients one afternoon weekly at his practice. I started with two hours of seeing one dog every ten minutes. Within a couple of years, this grew to twelve patients in every hour for six consecutive hours. Marc expanded the parking lot twice to accommodate the number of patients.

I also continued with my mornings at Donna's. It provided a venue for patients who were uncomfortable with other dogs, or people who were reluctant to bring their pets to a clinic. I also saw large numbers of litters at Donna's, and could readily recruit Savannah, or my niece Aidan, to help with restraining and note taking when a wiggly mass of eight to ten puppies was the lure. Many of my clients at Donna's persisted through several generations of dogs and would ask about the growing family with vested interest. They celebrated when the Logan they had held as a nursing baby grew to the 6'4" varsity basketball player some eighteen years later.

I was only offering chiropractic in Ottawa, but continued to maintain a regular veterinary practice in Pembroke. I was the only veterinarian willing to see exotic patients in the Ottawa Valley at that time. The poor front staff were challenged in the scheduling of my two specialties. Ten-minute chiro appointments were interspersed with twenty-minute beak trims, physical examinations of egg-bound birds, sluggish iguanas, and anorexic snakes. It made for lively and inevitably chaotic Wednesday afternoons.

I could stay on schedule for the chiro appointments, but the exotics always introduced an unpredictable element. I had a recurrent appointment for beak and nail trims of an African Grey parrot named "Index". He had been so named because he had amputated the second digit of his previous owner. He was a grumpy, screechy, large bird who required two people to properly restrain him while I used a Dremel to trim his nails and beak. Adrenaline ran high in the small exam room and we would all breathe a sigh of relief when we had completed the procedure with faces and hands intact. It would never stay within the allotted twenty minutes. The pay scale for the service was dictated by the veterinary fee guide. We would charge $14 for this life-threatening service.

Snakes created even greater havoc. There always seemed to be a receptionist or summer student who was ophidiophobic, absolutely terrified of snakes. I had to tend to a fainted student who knocked her head on the counter when a snake was scheduled with an eye infection. We were poorly equipped to dispense medication for reptiles and I would often have to concoct dilute versions of medicine formulated for cats and dogs.

Emergencies were problematic. Clients would sometimes wait a full week with pets in crisis. An egg-bound bird that should have been seen immediately, luckily survived the five-day wait to see me. She could easily have perished. The only other option was an expensive and time-consuming trip to a specialty clinic in Ottawa. Clients would choose the riskier but cheaper option, and wait to see me on Wednesdays. These emergencies were never easily resolved in the allotted time.

Don and Sybil came to visit from Germany for a one-week vacation with our family. Sybil elected to accompany me on one of my busy exotic-vet/chiro composite afternoons. The schedule was packed with a gerbil appointment and a cockatoo beak trim sandwiched between fifteen chiropractic visits. The gerbil, "Mountie", was losing weight and his family was concerned.

I picked him up and turned him over onto his back to palpate his little tummy. Unsurprisingly, Mountie was not a fan of this procedure and bit me hard, his teeth almost meeting in the middle of my pinky. I responded in the instinctive way that in no way reflected my education in exotics. I shook my hand vigorously, whipping the little guy violently into the corner of the examination room. With heart racing, I picked him up, ensuring that he was still alive. I'm sure his heart rate matched my own. Sybil gently took him from me when she noticed I was bleeding all over the little guy. I gave him a microscopic amount of a laxative, asked them to keep me apprised of his health, and quietly directed the staff to discount his exam fee.

I was, of course, late for all the subsequent appointments. I have since heard identical stories from several colleagues—including a chiropractor who was asked to adjust a mouse and threw him on the ground when he was bitten. In that case, the owners reported a miraculous recovery from the spinal injury that had led them to seek an animal chiro. I was just happy Mountie survived my hand flick.

Two weeks later, I was asked to remove the anal glands of a ferret. Each gland has to be carefully teased from the surrounding tissue and removed without breaking the smelly sac. One of the glands spilled as I excised it.

This resulted in an infection which required weeks of antibiotics. It undermined my confidence in my surgical skills, and had me question the wisdom of performing surgery once every few months. Surgery is a hand-eye skill that depends on regular practice to maintain dexterity and composure. In my first year of practice, I was comfortably doing five or six surgeries daily, with a respectable twenty-minute spay time.

When veterinarians return from holiday, surgical time is often a bit slower on the first Monday. Clearly, performing one surgery every few weeks was not ideal for my patients.

I started training a younger vet with an interest in exotic medicine. Kev and I were gearing up for a two-month mini sabbatical with the kids in Australia. I used the time away as a good exit plan from exotics and returned from our travels ready to focus uniquely on chiropractic.

Exotic Chiropractic Patients

RETREATING FROM THE WORLD OF regular medicine did not herald an end to my seeing exotics. All animals with spines are vulnerable to misalignments, and a number of them found their way into my office.

One of my regular Ottawa clients was a shaggy, black, friendly mutt belonging to Maria, an earthy vegan landscaper who was thrilled when I restored the bounce to her canine companion. One day, I found her sitting dejectedly in the waiting room, with a large cage on her lap. She showed me the contents, a bloated hamster called "Moose" lying listlessly among the cedar shavings. She said he hadn't had a bowel movement in three days and she was afraid of losing him. She asked if there was anything chiropractic that could relieve him.

I palpated him gingerly and felt a bulge at his fourth cervical vertebra, the subluxation I associated with colic in horses. I gently thrust on the bone and was rewarded with an immediate flattening of the bump. He pooped before leaving the clinic.

Maria would subsequently bring me two more hamsters, a rabbit, and a guinea pig for a variety of ailments. She would always trust my hands before more-invasive medical procedures. She remained enormously grateful despite that the cost of the adjustment usually exceeding the cost of the pocket pet.

My most terrifying chiropractic patient was a perky, bright-blue budgerigar called "Arthur". I had met Arthur before for wing trims and nail trims, always accompanied by both his elderly owners, Mr. and Mrs. Paget. He apparently had a vocabulary of more than twenty words. In the confines of a vet office, stress reduced his speech to "Stupid, stupid, stupid …" muttered in appropriately mumbling grumpy tones. I was surprised to see Arthur's name in my list of chiropractic appointments. I worried a staff was trying to reinsert me into my old role as an exotic vet.

It was immediately clear why he was scheduled. Arthur's head was twisted to the right as if he were checking his right shoulder. He could eat food that was proffered directly to his beak, but could not eat out of his food baskets. Arthur had been flying freely in his house and had flown into a glass door and fallen to the ground. The crash resulted in a pronounced torticollis.

I gave the elderly couple the same spiel I used to give before any treatment involving the handling of small birds. "These little guys have such a high metabolism, and are so prone to stress responses, that just restraining him could kill him. I will be as gentle as possible, but want you to know the risks ahead of time."

The Pagets comfortably signalled their permission for me to proceed. I had likely inured them of their anxiety with the identical speech every time I had trimmed Arthur's nails, beak and wings. In contrast, I was petrified as I gently palpated Arthur's neck. It was too small for any specificity in adjusting. I rotated his head to the left. We all heard a pop. I held my breath. Arthur moved his head from side to side, contorting to a definite non-mammalian arc of over a hundred degrees. His head was straight!

Arthur was the only pet bird I was ever asked to adjust. The experience allowed me the confidence to adjust turkeys on three separate occasions. One had been caught and released by a fox, and the next two had been injured in navigating through tight fences. I adjusted their necks successfully. Luckily, the injuries always involved the necks. I am not really sure how I would adjust the thorax or pelvis of a bird. It made for great hilarity at the family thanksgiving table to know that I had clients paying to have their turkeys adjusted. We all figured it was win-win. Either a resounding chiropractic success, or dinner!

I also had a chance to revisit the animal of my Calgary zoo cause for fame. A young woman arrived unscheduled at my busy Stittsville practice with a small carrier marked with the logo of the wildlife rehab centre in Ottawa. She begged the front staff to see if I would be willing to check out a squirrel for free. The squirrel had been hit by a car, and the driver had remarkably been motivated to stop. They had brought him to the centre wrapped in a scarf.

He had been nicknamed "Peanut" by the staff. He was flourishing with good food and warm housing, but could not be released as he had no ability to stand without listing to starboard. He would circle in the enclosure with head pressed against the Plexiglas leaving a trail of clean glass at a four-inch height. He could not perch on the branch of a tree they introduced into the cage. He had been at the centre for two weeks with a growing number of young fans among the teenage volunteers.

I warily positioned my hands to reach his neck. I was fully anticipating a squirming biter who would do more damage than the gerbil with the needle teeth that had left a tiny scar on my pinky. Jenny, the centre volunteer who had brought Peanut in and who had initiated the idea of getting him adjusted, was armed with thick leather gloves as she held his body prone. He squirmed against the resistance.

When my hands circled his atlas, he went absolutely still. I could hardly feel any space between atlas and occiput on the right side. The bone adjusted with minimal pressure.

Jenny brought him back for a recheck the following week, but it was not truly necessary. Peanut had gone back to his enclosure that first day and was able to cavort all over the cage, no head pressing and no problems balancing on the branch. He was released in front of a class of grade 8 students that afternoon with much fanfare.

A cool appendix to the story was Jenny's reaction. She called me several months later to let me know she had reached a career impasse in her job in high-tech a year earlier. She had been volunteering at the wildlife centre while debating her next step. After witnessing Peanut's recovery, she had elected to apply to vet school in her home province of P.E.I. She was going to pursue a career in animal chiropractic. She sent me a thank you card when she was accepted to the vet program. I can only presume that she's busy and happily adjusting animals in the Maritimes now.

Cows!

MY FIRST REAL ENCOUNTER WITH cows was my first visit to Kev's parents' farm.

Kevin's younger brother, Denis, had picked me up at the bus stop in the nearest town and he and Kevin had teased me on the twenty-minute drive, pulling into the driveway of a pink clapboard house, claiming it was the homestead, and identifying the farmers in the fields as their parents. Each joke fed my fears. I knew that I had been labelled as a Westmount City Snob, a moniker I despised. I was also the "new girl-friend", hot on the heels of a steady girlfriend of three years.

We pulled into a dirt lane and parked at the gate. Kev and Denis strad-dled the fence and walked boldly through a herd of bulls. I was very impressed. I knew they were bulls because of the massive horns on their giant heads. Never one to walk away from a challenge, I gamely clam-bered over the fence and gingerly waded through the herd.

I gather I should have let my eyes wander immodestly lower to see the full udders on these "bulls". I had just sadly fulfilled all expectations of a Westmount City Girl! I spent the next two days mucking out an old barn from two years of accumulated hard-packed chicken shit. Appar-ently, that redeemed me in Kevin's parents' eyes.

The encounter predated my years at vet school. There was no such thing as streaming in those days. All one hundred students in my class graduated with skills in handling aggressive stallions, restraining feral cats, taking blood from a parrot, and manoeuvring reluctant cows into a corral. Even the most cat loving, manicured and prissy of my classmates learned the best way to halter a cow, how to milk from an inflamed teat, and the perfect pitch to whistle while rubbing the perineum of a cow to provoke a stream of urine to sample.

When I first graduated and practised mixed animal medicine in the Valley, there was ample opportunity to test my newly minted knowledge of cow medicine. There are moments of glory in being a cow vet. The placid beasts are generally pleasant to work with, and the farmers are friendly and often offer a coffee or slice of pie after a farm call. But it is a shitty job, literally. Once the glow of being an actual vet, donning blue coveralls, and arriving at midnight to save a calf or relieve a bloat are over, the shine fades quickly from cow medicine.

Cows are considered income-generating units. They are rarely afforded the affection and level of individual medicine that pets command. The work is generally stinky and messy, the bill is reluctantly paid and often questioned, and much of the work is on an emergency basis. A lot of farmers do their own vetting, choosing to call in an expert only when things are spiralling downwards.

When I gave up my position in the mixed animal practice, I figured I was happily finished with cow medicine.

Early in my animal chiropractic career, I was called by a parent of one of Savannah's classmates in kindergarten.

"We have a cow who can't move her tail," Anna explained. "Our vet couldn't find any good reason why and suggested we call you."

I dragged my coveralls out of hibernation and headed to the farm, a vast dairy operation. The cow was a large Holstein, easily picked out with a roached back, limp tail, and massively fecal-stained bum. Having lost the ability to raise her tail meant that the cow was pooping all over her rear rather than pushing out a satisfying cow patty.

Cows have big lumbar vertebrae with overlapping lateral processes. The spinal architecture gives them good solidity, but makes adjusting them a challenge. I palpated her lower back and found the sacrum to be tilted and the sixth lumbar vertebra seemed to dive down toward her feet. No amount of motion palpating would elicit any movement. The cow was getting a bit pissed off, too.

I needed to lift the vertebra somehow.

I was fresh enough from my vet schooling to think laterally. "Do you have any rectal sleeves?" I asked.

I stretched the long plastic gloves over my hand and elbow, tucking the edges under my bra strap. No amount of securing seems to protect one's shoulders or hair from the inevitable soiling with cow poo, though. An essential part of vet education is learning to do rectal palpations. It takes special skill to gently run gloved fingers through rectal walls to discern the fluid filled follicles on an ovary. This is done while the upper arm is squeezed relentlessly in the vice of anal muscles straining against the foreign arm. It was one area of male-dominated medicine where the long slim arms of lanky females was an advantage. It is not a glamorous skill, but is a gratifying one when you can have an arm disappear into the rectum of a cow and then proclaim, like a soothsayer, on her reproductive status.

I thought I had retired from my days of gloved examinations. Muscle memory guided me as I applied globs of lube to my gloved hand and finessed my way into the rectum of the cow. Anna obligingly held the limp tail away from me. I ignored the reproductive organs and focused on the bony structures. I could feel the lower prominences of the lumbar vertebrae. I made a fist and pushed hard on the one that seemed to pro-trude much more ventrally than the adjacent vertebrae. It moved.

I can't claim any high velocity thrust or specificity to the adjustment, but Anna immediately declared "Wow. She's pulling a bit with her tail now."

I did get a pastry and coffee for my efforts, and Anna proclaimed me a genius at the next parent–teacher night. Typical of services rendered for an acquaintance, that was the extent of my remuneration.

The next time I was called out for a cow, I made sure I was clear about the cost from the start. It was again an acquaintance. Cow medicine was not something I advertised or encouraged. The call came from a patient of Kevin's, Samantha. She described a gimpy cow, one of their favourites, a good milker, and a reliable mom. She had started to have a hitch to her gait and a marked decrease in milk production after a difficult calving.

After Samantha had finished relaying information about the cow, she then said that it was awkward, and that I shouldn't schedule her any time soon. She assured me that it wasn't the price that daunted her. She waffled for a few moments, obviously recognizing that she sounded insincere.

"Ok, I'll be honest," she finally said. "Bruce didn't want me to make this call. He thinks I'm cracked to think about getting her adjusted." She assured me she would work on him. She just wanted to ensure that I would treat a cow if asked.

I had almost forgotten about the cow when the call did come. It was at least five months later.

"Are you free today?" Samantha asked apologetically. "I know it's very last minute, but Bruce is sick. He's flat out with the flu. He'll never know you came."

It wasn't ideal. I bundled the kids in the car, gathering snacks to keep them occupied. I wondered about the ethics of treating an animal with permission from only one owner, and possibly not the key owner in a herd where the milk quota was so often inherited through the male line. I was motivated by hoping to help a cow who had now suffered from a five-month complaint.

She was housed in the typical slurry of mud and manure. My running shoes were ill equipped for the job. I approached and patted her, starting as usual from the head to build a relationship before addressing her wonky hips. The big beast was very docile and tractable, and let me palpate her lumbar spine and massive pin bones, the tuber ischia, which make a cow's rear a large bony square. There was absolutely no movement in the left sacroiliac joint. I leveraged onto the lower rung of the fence and gave my biggest thrust. There was no resounding clunk, but I was rewarded with a nice-bouncy feeling hip.

I told Samantha I'd take payment in some organic meat for my non-vegetarian mate. No point in taking a cheque which would announce her transgression to poor sick Bruce.

She 'fessed up anyway. He commented immediately the next week when both the cow's gait and milk yield seemed mysteriously restored. To his credit, this staunchly conservative farmer became a vocal proponent for chiropractic care and stopped grumbling about the cost of Samantha's treatment at Kev's office as well.

One of my lecturers at the animal chiropractic school had built a reputation in California by adjusting milking cows and measurably increasing milk production. Ontario is governed by a milk quota system in which any increase in yield is not really rewarded. So my practice did not veer into the world of dairy farms. I happily stayed focused on performance and pet practice with about fifty percent of my patient load coming from horses, and the remainder from small animal, mainly dogs.

I have probably adjusted one or two cows annually in the past twenty years, as well as the odd llama, goat, and donkey. Generally, it's because the animal had been elevated to pet status, rather than herd component. One client, Kim, moved from childhood 4-H club to the world of agricultural fairs. Kim regularly has her prize cow adjusted before competition in world fairs. These are not the fly-covered, manure-coated cows off the field. These cows are shampooed to shiny perfection, groomed, and handled like well-schooled ponies. They are always a pleasure to handle. The heifer I first adjusted for Kim went on to place first in North America. Ever since, she finds some reason—an awkward gait, or minor roach, or swayback—to justify having me out to tune up her candidate.

I have adjusted some notable champion dogs and horses. There is always a queue of performance horses and racers looking for a legal edge to attain the winners circle. Likewise, the canine world has generated a steady stream of dogs competing in agility and conformation where an adjustment makes them more competitive. I suspect my highest achieving patient was still the heifer who won the North American title.

The Economics of Love

I WAS DRAWN TO VETERINARY medicine by my love of animals. I soon discovered that it was vastly upstaged by my clients' level of commitment to their pets. Some clients would mortgage their houses, literally, to save their pets.

There was an economic chasm between Pembroke and Ottawa that was greater than the hundred and forty or so kilometres that separated them. The love and sacrifice I regularly saw in my practice were evident in both groups. They just manifested differently.

"Don't tell your husband that I brought Fern to see you today," Mrs. Todd would advise me in a stage whisper. "I had to cancel my appointment with him, you see. I can only afford one of you this week, and it seemed like Fern needed you more. I can live with my cranky back for another week or two."

In Ottawa, dogs were brought in by nannies and dog sitters when owners couldn't take the time off work. I told one couple that their dog should avoid stairs while he recuperated from a herniated disk. They proudly announced on their subsequent visit that they had managed to sell their house. They had purchased a one-story bungalow with nary a stair to challenge their dog's recovery.

One little Maltese, "Sprite", taught me about making sexist assumptions.

She was an older, arthritic dog with poor vision and a weak bladder.

Her owner was Mai Wong, a lovely older lady with limited English. She insisted on bringing Sprite to me weekly, claiming she was so much happier and moved better after each visit. I was very conscious of the economic toll of the weekly visits, and would advise fewer visits. I wrote "recommended recheck in three to four weeks" in the clinic notes. Despite the notes, Sprite would be there to greet me every Tuesday, usually booked as the first patient of the afternoon, and often arriving half an hour before I got there.

One day, Sprite was accompanied by a middle-aged gentleman who introduced himself as Mai's husband. Sprite's eyes, always blue with cataracts, were inflamed, oozing and crusted closed. Mr. Wong said they had spent the night at the 24-hour emergency clinic and were treating Sprite for a melting ulcer. He had taken her out for the chiropractic treatment, but was going to bring her back to the clinic for surgery.

I made a sympathetic comment about the cost of this new hurdle in Sprite's declining health. I figured he was willing to pay these exorbitant fees for Mai's geriatric dog because of his love for his wife. When I looked up from adjusting Sprite, I was arrested by Mr. Wong's face. He was ashen and started to cry.

"I hope we didn't wait too long," he stammered. "We feel so bad, so very, very bad for her. We do the surgery tonight. You think she hurting? Does she need more pain medicine? And she do so well when you treat her. We want to come two times a week. We pay extra, no problem."

I realized I had just met the more emotionally vested member of the family. I reassured him that it looked like Sprite's pain was being well-managed and that once a week was more than adequate for keeping her in alignment.

Sprite would go on to have three eye surgeries, likely costing more than a house down-payment. She also continued with a regime of weekly adjustments until she was well into her eighteenth year. She loved me and basked in the adjustments, always walking out of the clinic when she was usually carried in. I always got a teary hug from Mr. Wong and a stammered thank you for keeping Sprite going. I dreaded the day she would be so pain filled and decrepit that I would have to recommend euthanasia. Mr. and Mrs. Wong remained completely attuned to her needs to the end. They elected to have her euthanized at home when she could no longer rise to greet them one morning. I wrote them a long letter, a testimonial to both Sprite and their unflagging devotion to her. I never saw them again.

"Doc" was similarly loved. He was a crotchety, opinionated horse in his early teens when I first met him. He had been confined to stall rest because of a tendon injury. Caroline, his devoted owner, had devised a series of clicker commands to keep him occupied and entertained.

"Show me the pear, Doc," she would croon, holding up a pear in one hand and an apple in the other. She would reward him with a click and a carrot when he nudged the right fruit. He could identify a square versus a circle, a halter versus a bridle, and count to five with foot stomps. He tolerated Caroline's friends, disliked strangers, and adored Caroline.

I was initially an unwelcome intruder. He pinned his ears and tried to bite me when I entered the convalescent's stall. After his first adjustment, he mellowed and tolerated my ministrations as long as Caroline kept bribing him with carrot pieces. He grew to so anticipate the relief of the adjustments that he would immediately get an erection when I arrived. Caroline laughingly referred to it as the "chiropractic fifth leg".

I adjusted Doc for almost twenty years. He never seemed to age. He could cavort like a colt enough to scare a similarly aging Caroline into long lunge sessions before mounting him. I adjusted him every eight weeks. Caroline never hesitated to call and add an extra session if he had fallen, or had dentistry, or had developed a limp. He was a venerable thirty years old when he passed due to an unresponsive colic rather than any symptom of old age. It was the loss of a family member.

The biggest bonus of a chiropractic practice is helping patients in families where they are treasured. I was cocooned in a world where people didn't question the economics of helping relieve suffering. Back in my regular vet days, I had clients weigh the costs of resolving a blocked bladder in their cat against the cost of euthanasia. Luckily the relatively cheap cost of chiropractic and the nature of the clients seeking the service meant that cost was rarely discussed or challenged. I also got to know and love both patients and their owners because of the repeat nature of the visits. For an introvert, it could be challenging. But I emerged from busy afternoons feeling like I had just met up with forty or more close friends.

The Christmas Village

I PULLED INTO THE DRIVEWAY, late at night, navigating our icy stairs with difficulty. I was lugging a large cardboard box filled with gaily wrapped Christmas presents. It was my last Tuesday adjusting dogs before Christmas, and the season had inspired a bounty of cards and gifts from my chiropractic clients.

The kids greeted me enthusiastically. My arrival meant we could sit to eat as a family. Kevin was a champion at getting supper ready on my late nights. They were excitedly poring through the box of gifts from my patients. These were presents they were allowed to open long before the morning of the 25th.

There was the usual cornucopia of wine and chocolates, the latter generating a more positive response than the former from my three eager kids. The box that really caught their fancy, though, was a large box meticulously wrapped in shiny paper. It was torn apart quickly to reveal a Styrofoam box, securely taped. They pulled that apart, too. The treasure within drew gasps of delight. It was a miniature, old-fashioned veterinary clinic, with a long-skirted lady holding a dog at the end of a leash glued onto its front steps. There was a cord attached. We plugged it in and the scene inside the house could now be viewed through the Victorian pane windows. A veterinarian in a white lab coat could be seen bending over a large dog at an examining table, stethoscope in hand.

We set it under the Christmas tree. It was from Colette, a very sweet, diminutive lady from Belgium, who regularly brought her French bull-dog "Hercules" to see me at the Ottawa clinic. Hercules was typical of the breed. He had the winning sunny disposition that continues to persuade people to invest in the breed. They are otherwise beset with spinal issues, hemivertebrae, spinal stenosis, and a propensity for joint disease. They snuffle and snort due to their brachycephalic short noses, have diffi-culties with heat, and are prone to heart disease. The spinal issues dictate that I have had a number of Frenchies as patients. They do exceedingly well with chiropractic, and function best with regular preventive care rather than the quick fix of patients with acute injuries. I tended to make fast friends with these committed and very loving owners.

Hercules initially presented at my clinic with hind leg paralysis. His breeder, a veterinarian and very conscientious breeder who tried to minimize the health risks of the breed with selective couplings, had referred him to me. The adjustments had restored him to walking within two weeks. He still walked with a rounded back and had radiographic evidence of hemivertebrae and collapsed disks, so Colette and her hus-band brought Hercules to get adjusted every month. He had been symptom free for several years with this protocol.

I saw Colette three weeks after Christmas and told her how much our whole family had appreciated her generous gift. Her husband, Bernard, was with her, and he laughed.

"*Tu devrais voir notre maison pendant la saison de Noël*," he said proudly. He and Colette could both cope in English but were delighted to speak French with me. He told me their house became a shrine to an enormous Christmas village every year. Colette would start to set it up in early November in order to have it fully functional by Christmas.

The following December, Colette brought me another gaily wrapped box. The kids opened it expectantly. Sure enough, it housed a second miniature house, this time an old-fashioned pet store. We set it up proudly beside the veterinary clinic. Colette had enclosed a Christmas card where she included her home address and an invitation to bring the family to inspect her "village".

Kev and I were in Ottawa early December with the kids to help decorate my mother's Christmas tree. On our way home, we detoured through Stittsville to see Colette's collection. Hercules greeted me enthusiastically when we rang the doorbell. We were ushered into a living room divided by a one-foot-high picket fence. Behind the fence, protected from Hercules's rambunctious antics, was a vast expanse of more than fifty houses lined up in discrete blocks and separated by streets with operating streetlights. There was a miniature train wending through the town, and the scene was crowned by a cathedral on a "snow"-covered hill. Colette showed us how the Gordian Knot of power cords was hidden discreetly under a swath of cotton snow. When we entered her kitchen to enjoy cookies and hot chocolate, she showed us that the entire sunroom was an extension of further houses. I upped my estimate of house number to closer to several hundred. It was a collection worthy of a museum.

Colette gave me a candy shop house the following year. Sadly, Hercules succumbed to heart disease in the next year. He was fourteen years old. He had outlived his breed average by a good two years.

When we pulled out our three Christmas village houses the next year, the kids persuaded me to buy a new addition: a Victorian mansion. This became a tradition for the subsequent fifteen years. Our Christmas tree is now girdled by a village of twenty or so houses, twinkling with lights, and magical when all the other lights are extinguished. It is an enchanting show that never fails to invite inspection by our nieces and nephews. I love setting it up every year, likely a throwback to my obsession with the little horse village that dominated my childhood bedroom.

I never saw Colette or Bernard after Hercules passed, and I suspect they didn't opt to replace him. I think of them annually when I unpack my village, which takes more and more room in our storage boxes in the barn. The little dog in front of the miniature vet clinic has a chipped ear and looks more like a lab than a Frenchie, but I have forever dubbed him Hercules.

Puppies!

A CHORUS OF WILD BARKING was triggered by ringing the doorbell at a client's house. An even louder shrieking of "Will you SHUT UP?" followed. The request went unheeded and nine dogs milled around me eagerly when the door was opened by Belinda.

I had agreed to adjust the newest additions to Belinda's menagerie. The cacophony was the result of nine adult dogs, one recent postpartum female, and nine one-week-old puppies, all sharing space in a relatively small split-level home. The nine adults were running in and out of the kitchen animatedly. It looked like I had interrupted feeding time.

Belinda pulled open the child's gate barricading the stairs. The puppies were up in her bedroom. She apologized for the level of chaos. She said she had not slept many hours in two or three days.

"Muggy", a beautiful Keeshond I had been adjusting for years, looked up nervously when I entered the room. She rose to her feet, dislodging several of the puppies who were actively nursing. High-pitched mewling protests followed. Muggy climbed over the cardboard rim of the whelping box and settled comfortably on the floor beside me, looking very content to be free of the nine miniature ravenous mouths of her offspring.

I adjusted Muggy first. The pups had been delivered naturally, but she had experienced a prolonged labour with a four-hour break between the first six pups, followed by one still birth, and then the final three. I was not surprised to find her very subluxated in her pelvic girdle. She adjusted like butter. The hormone relaxin, which eases delivery, was still coursing through her veins, making her pelvic girdle compliant and mobile.

We then started working our way through the pups. The first two that Belinda presented were perfect. We moved each pup to the enclosure where Muggy lay. They latched on happily. The maternal coffee break was over. The third pup's atlas was markedly out of alignment. Belinda picked him up and examined his feet after I adjusted him, before lowering him to the floor to join the nursing siblings.

"That is purple toe," she announced with satisfaction. She had marked all the toes of the pups with identifying blotches of nail polish. "He was the first one out and gave no end of a struggle with his big head. I had to help Vaseline his way out. I'm not surprised he had a neck problem."

The next two had clear spines, and the seventh had a minor mid-thoracic subluxation which corrected with finger pressure. The eighth puppy, however, was smaller than his siblings and had three vertebrae out of alignment in his neck. His feet were marked with green nail polish.

"Poor thing," crooned Belinda, as she cradled the tiny pup while I adjusted him. "I don't know if he'll make it. He isn't gaining much weight and I certainly can't sell or breed him. Look how undershot he is."

I hadn't paid much attention to his jaw in my focus on the spine. I opened his mouth, and sure enough, the lower teeth extended far beyond his upper teeth, a condition labelled prognathia in veterinary lingo. I palpated the temporal-mandibular joint. It was wedged bilaterally with a marked swelling around the joint. I adjusted the joint, doing a reverse modified jaw thrust, more by intuition than learning.

The joint moved. Neither Belinda nor I could discern any appreciable change in the jaw after the adjustment, though. We added him to the group of nursing pups, and I checked the last pup and declared her perfect.

I adjusted the noisy crew downstairs. Belinda was delighted to have the entire household adjusted once I was there. She usually brought her dogs to the clinic in pairs or trios. Any more was a challenge for transport.

I agreed to return in one month to check the pups before they were re-homed and to adjust the entire group again.

I brought Savannah with me on my return trip. My children have all been very clear about their lack of enthusiasm for vet medicine. I destroyed any temptation with too many "volun-told" hours taking notes in cold barns. But one cannot underestimate the lure of a litter of puppies. A ten-year-old Savannah was thrilled to accompany me and take notes.

We were again greeted by the chorus of barking and "SHUT UP. SHUT UP. The lot of you!"

Sav grinned. I had told her in advance to expect this loud reception. Belinda opened the door. She wore a smug expression.

"Come in, come in," she urged. "Let's go straight up to the pups. I can't wait to show you!"

The puppies were much bigger and fuzzier. They were at their peak of cuteness. I heard Sav gasp in adoration. I knew I would have a rough time convincing her to leave empty handed.

"They are all sold. Right?" I prompted Belinda.

She answered truthfully, "I'm afraid so. In fact, I have a waiting list. My next litter is all spoken for, too!"

She smiled at my clearly disappointed daughter.

"Let me show you something special, Savannah" She reached into the swarm of lively pups and pulled out one of them. She flipped him over.

We could all see the green dab of nail polish on his hind toe.

"Look closely" she advised me. "Check out his jaw. Am I imagining it? Doesn't it look completely normal to you?"

The puppy's lower jaw lined up fully with the upper jaw. The teeth met midline with no discernible overlap. The little guy had filled out. He now matched his siblings in stature.

"Crazy, huh? And to think for years I just gave pups like this away after making sure they were neutered. I always thought it was a genetic abnormality. You vets always told me that, in fact." This, she uttered accusingly.

I was floored. I had never thought an adjustment could affect bone growth so radically.

I started offering full-litter checks regularly after being schooled by the little prognathic pup. I saw a number of jaw abnormalities resolve, scissor jaws, overbites and underbites, and some roached or scoliotic pups who benefited from early adjustments. I also was braver in adjusting foals with congenital abnormalities like contracted tendons, and windswept foals with exaggerated angled limbs. Not all improved, but a large number did so well that it educated me about the plasticity of bones in early development, and the value in providing chiropractic care to the very young.

The Family of Crazy Injuries and Animals

I MANOEUVRED MY RAV4 CAREFULLY down the dirt driveway. I had to avoid two brilliantly coloured and aggressively posturing peacocks who blocked the drive. A llama and a camel poked their heads over the fence when I climbed out of the car. I was curious what type of patient was awaiting me.

I was welcomed warmly at the house by a white-haired, animated woman in her late seventies. She introduced herself as Bobby Maclean. She threw on a pair of rubber boots and accompanied me to the barn. The barn looked empty but when Bobby called out "Pippa?" a blonde woman around my age unfurled herself from the floor of one of the stalls. She had been sitting behind an emaciated horse that raised its head wearily at our entry.

"I hope you can do some magic," was Pippa's dour greeting. "This girl is going downhill fast. I've heard good things about you, even though my vet thinks I'm kind of crazy to spend money on horse chiro. But I'm kind of stuck. And besides, nothing he has done for her has helped one iota."

She explained that the mare belonged to her fourteen-year-old daughter. She had purchased the mare after long deliberation and a rigorous search on the 'net. But the horse had flipped out at being loaded onto the trailer and had gone over backwards when she reared. They had managed to bring her home, but she had not eaten since.

"I think she's down a good two hundred pounds! The only food we can get into her has to be offered by hand. You found me trying to get her to eat some hay, but it's a kind of slow process, handful by handful. My daughter has more patience, but she's at school all day."

We urged the mare to her feet. She was a classy-looking black Thoroughbred, but her eyes were dull and her coat had lost its gloss. She was clearly languishing with the calorie deficit. I felt her atlas. This is always the bone I first palpate. This one was crazy, hot and unmoving. I moved my hands along the next two vertebrae. Again, there was no motion and the segments were hot to touch.

"When did this happen?" I asked.

I was told the accident was six days earlier. I had taken the "not eating" to be hyperbole. The weight loss and inflamed segments suggested that Pippa was not exaggerating. I leveraged my hand behind the wing of the atlas and adjusted. It would have been ideal to see radiographs of the neck vertebrae, but that was beyond the scope and economics of equine medicine in the Valley. I had to reassure myself with a thorough palpating of the segment that there was no vertebral fracture or dislocation.

The adjustment produced the audible crack that often scares the uninitiated. Pippa looked unperturbed. She was clearly a chiropractic patient. The second and third vertebrae went in unison when I flexed the mare's neck toward me. Before I could continue to the rest of her spine, the mare, unimaginatively called "Blackie", started to arch her head to the left and then to the right. She shook her head vigorously, creating more cracking noises as different vertebrae were mobilized. She then lowered her head and started eating nonchalantly on the pile of hay that lay on the floor.

"Holy moly," breathed Bobby. "There's the piece of magic you asked for, isn't it, Pippa?"

We stood around with satisfaction watching Blackie eat. I opted to not adjust her any further that day. I didn't want anything to compromise her recovery. Besides, she was so thin, I figured a bit of extra weight and muscle would be useful before I did any major thrusting on her thoracic or lumbar spine. Pippa started pulling out other horses which she deemed needed adjusting. Bobby added a miniature horse to the list.

I had finished and was enjoying a tour of the exotic menagerie of pot-bellied pigs, goats, llamas, and the one camel, when a school bus pulled up at the end of the lane. I met Lily, Pippa's attractive and very grown-up teen. When Lily saw Blackie eating, she shed the mature taciturn facade and started crying. She thanked me profusely as she hugged her horse.

Serendipitously, one of the other horses I adjusted for Pippa had an abscess break open the night after I adjusted him, resolving a lameness issue that had waxed and waned for months. I was suddenly the flavour of the month for the entire family. When I returned the following month, there were seven horses scheduled for me to adjust. Pippa had three, Bobby had one mini, and Pippa's two sisters, alliteratively named Penny and Pamela, had a couple horses each to round out the list. As I was leaving, I was pressed into promising to return monthly.

I learned to schedule extra time for Bobby's family. There was always a lengthy list of horses to adjust, with the odd dog or miniature horse tossed into the mix. Sadly, I was never recruited to adjust the camel or llamas. They were performance motivated, and the exotics were uniquely for the unusual animal exhibits at summer fairs. Chiropractic was reserved for the horses which had to earn their ribbons in eventing, driving, and dressage. The family competed fiercely, often vying with each other for top marks in the different classes, not caring when it meant unseating a sister or cousin in the rankings. It turned out the competition took a macabre note at Christmas.

"I was going to win," complained Pippa. "And then Mom had to go and break her leg dismounting and tripping over the mounting block."

I had been greeted that day by the ever-cheerful Bobby sporting a pair of crutches and a graffiti-covered plaster cast on her lower leg.

"Yup!" agreed Bobby. "Pippa thought she'd win with the three broken ribs from falling off Reuben. But we all thought three ribs was kind of a lame win."

I was completely bewildered as they hastened to explain. Every year at Christmas, a family member took home the trophy for the most catastrophic injury sustained that year. The prize had been awarded annually for over ten years, and the three daughters, the grandchildren, and Bobby and her husband had all won at various times.

"Penny thought she had it in the bag last year with the shoulder dislocation, but Lily one-upped her right before the holidays by crashing into the arena wall when her pony bucked her off. She split her head open and scared the bejeezus out of Dad." Pippa laughed. "She was dripping blood and needed ten stitches. I think that was her second concussion that year, too."

They agreed that their dad's hernia and a nephew's spinal fracture didn't count.

"Joe got his from driving too fast and skidding off the road, and Dad's is just from being old!" scoffed Pippa. "You have to get the injury from a horse to count."

It put a positive spin on horse misfortunes. One year, I saw so many horse-rider injuries that I Googled the risks. It turns out that it is twenty times more dangerous to ride a horse than it is to ride a motorcycle, with a chance of severe injury once every three hundred and fifty rides. It was no surprise that the award for biggest injury in the Maclean family never went uncollected.

Talk at Expo

As word spread about this weird profession, I was asked to give talks at a number of venues: 4-H clubs, dog obedience classes, and pony clubs.

One invitation seemed particularly tempting. I was asked to talk about animal chiropractic at the Exhibition in Ottawa. This was a popular carnival, held in the centre of town, with an agricultural fair sharing space with a wide array of amusement park rides. Along with a stipend for the presentation, I was offered free entry into the amusement park. This was an invitation I knew my children would not want me to pass up. The kids and I are all big fans of fast, exciting rides. Kevin tends to vote for holding the cotton candy and waiting for us at the ride exits. We gave him the day off and set off as a foursome.

We arrived an hour early, so I had a chance to ride on some of the roller coasters with the kids, as well as peruse the venue. Once we had a good feel of the geography of the area, I put Savannah in charge of her brothers and gave them free rein with their park pass to experience all the rides. I doled out some money for cotton candy, popcorn, and one chance each at winning a stuffed animal at the carnival games.

I went off in search of my talk locale. I discovered that I was to speak in the centre of a noisy circular tent ringed by vendors. People were milling in the area in chatty and haphazard groups. I reluctantly opened up my duffel bag holding my speech props: a plastic model of a spine, a stuffed child's toy of a horse, and brochures explaining my profession. I tried to project my voice over the white noise. It was impossible. People looked curiously at the woman speaking as if to herself in the middle of the dusty large tent. I felt as awkward as a kindergarten child doing my first public speaking stint in a hostile auditorium.

I abandoned my bag in the centre of the room, apologized to the "crowd" of two or three who had politely approached to hear me speak, and went off in search of a microphone.

The adjacent tent housed a collection of animals performing in the exhibition. There was a stadium jumping display scheduled in the afternoon, as well as some driving displays of working horses. I was struck with an inspiration.

"Would anyone like their horse examined and adjusted for free?" I announced loudly.

One beefy, bald man approached with a sceptical look. "What will it do?" he asked.

I gave him a brief description of what a horse adjustment can do.

A bearded man sidled closer as I spoke. "She can check out Bono," he told his friend. "That bloody idiot won't let me touch his head. It took three of us to get the bloody halter on this morning. No way are we going to get him into harness for three o'clock. It can't hurt." He suddenly looked a bit worried. "Or can it?"

I assured them that I hadn't hurt a horse yet in twelve years of adjusting.

They then gestured to a massive black Friesian standing in a small enclosure. They attached a lead to the lower ring on the halter. True to the bearded man's claim, the gelding raised his head aggressively when the halter was restrained.

Both men accompanied me to the centre ring. The reception was dramatically different. The gelding pranced as he entered, a juxtaposition of gleaming muscles with the elegant high-stepping gait of the breed. He tossed his head angrily with every step, forcing the bearded man to step lightly under the horse's much bigger feet. The milling crowd silenced and parted to allow an unobstructed path for the horse. Parents swept up their smaller children onto their backs or in arms, both for protection and for a better view.

I asked the bearded man to introduce himself and the horse, and let the crowd know why he had volunteered this horse for a chiropractic demonstration.

"I'm Bill, and this here is Big Bono. And this is John. John owns Bono. I just train him. Bono is normally a sweet-tempered guy, but when we got him off the trailer from Hudson, he was as cranky as a mule. He fusses when I groom him or do anything with his head. I don't know what he did, but he needs some kind of fixing. I see a chiropractor myself, so I know that they know their stuff. My chiro gets rid of my headaches, so I'm ready to trust this here girl and see if she can help old Bono."

I reached for the halter and Bono reared. I had everyone's attention now! I turned my back on Bono and studiously ignored him as I started talking about the cervical spines of horses. I engaged a girl who looked to be around ten years old and asked her how many neck vertebrae she thought a horse had. She guessed twelve. I told her they had seven, just like she did, and also amazingly just like a dolphin and a giraffe. As I spoke, I slowly put my hand on the lower part of Bono's neck and gently rubbed him over his shoulders, still looking away. He was trembling but didn't flinch away.

I started talking about the nasty effects of a neck subluxation: headaches, mood shifts, difficulty with balance, and difficulties in clearing ear and sinus infections. My hand snaked up Bono's neck, slowly palpating each segment in turn. There was no movement at the junction between the second and third vertebrae. I asked everyone to be as quiet as mice. The audience had grown and vendors had abandoned their stalls to join the growing circled crowd. I let Bono sniff my left hand and held the lower strap of the halter loosely as I urged his neck to the left. I placed the meat of my right hand at the fourth cervical vertebral body. One quick thrust. *Crack!*

The ten-year-old girl jumped back, startled.

Bono immediately relaxed in my left hand. He lowered his head toward me. His eyes were a luminescent brown, no longer white and wide. Everyone had heard the loud crack. I no longer needed a microphone to project my voice. All ears were tuned. I explained that the crack was merely the sound of gas exiting the joint cavitation, much like the snapping sound of popcorn being made. I moved my hand up to cradle Bono's enormous head and palpated both sides to compare the distance between the skull and first cervical vertebrae. There was no gap whatsoever on the left. I invited Bill and John to examine it themselves, placing their fingers in the correct spots. They agreed in surprise as they felt the disparity.

Bono was getting restless with the groping. I reached up and tugged his head to the left over my left shoulder as I thrust at the wide wing of the atlas. This produced an even louder crack. Bono twisted his head to the right and then left, and then reached back and scratched at his left flank with his teeth.

I didn't need to explain to the audience that he was wallowing in his newly restored mobility. If a horse could grin, Bono was grinning!

I adjusted the rest of his spine with less drama. I gave an improvised version of my talk as I adjusted, explaining at each segment what misalignments could affect, both in people and in horses.

Bill and John were more voluble when I finished. They explained that they had experienced awful traffic en route to Ottawa. John said he had stopped abruptly several times to avoid collisions, and they could hear both Bono and his partner horse crashing about behind their truck. The other horse had not looked too perturbed when they'd arrived at the exhibition, but Bono had been sweaty and difficult to handle. We agreed it was likely that Bono had been whiplashed by one of the rapid stops.

I finished the talk and assumed I could answer a few questions and then rejoin the kids. But a second horse was led into the area and I was asked to repeat the process with a jumper who had a difficult time landing on her left lead. The mare was quiet and much less of a spectacle than Bono had been. Many of the crowd remained during the second demonstration, and new people drifted in to join the first group. The crowd would have been dangerously close to the initially flighty Bono, but the mare didn't object to having an audience.

I fielded questions for over half an hour when I finished. I exhausted my supply of brochures, booked several stables on the spot, and also referred hordes of people to my brother and sister-in-law, Keith and Andrea, who practised human chiropractic in Ottawa.

I found Savannah, Forest, and Logan sitting at the edge of the auditorium when the crowd finally thinned. They had gotten bored of the rides and were ready to go home.

The day had started with one of the worst speaking engagements I had ever experienced, and ended with an enormously positive one. The kids had enjoyed the rides and were stuffed with carnival junk food and candy. We all deemed it a huge success. But when I was approached and asked to speak the following year, I declined. I figured the serendipity of finding a Bono, the perfect patient, in an adjacent tent was highly unlikely. I had no desire to once again be speaking mutely in an arena with a loud and completely indifferent crowd.

Invaluable Help

THE ROAD WAS SWIMMING IN front of me, a blur of mesmerizing white dots. I pulled over, turned on my hazards, and lay my head on the steering wheel.

"Wake up, chica!" I admonished myself. I rolled the window wide open and blared some music from a teenage rock channel. I had been driving on the Queens Line, twelve kilometres of a straight, farm-edged road. It was 10 PM and I had been driving or adjusting since 6:30 that morning. The blizzard had hit around thirty kilometres from home and the hour remaining of my drive was now stretching into its second hour. It was hard to make out where the road and shoulder joined.

When I made it in the door, I was greeted by a hot fire in the wood stove, and a sympathetic Kevin. The kids were already in bed.

"I need to change something," I said as I collapsed into the chair and accepted a medicinal glass of Cinzano from Kev. "I think I need a driver."

I am not a happy driver, either at the wheel or as a passenger. I hate sitting. I had thought to minimize the hours in the car by scheduling all closely located stables in the same working day. As my practice grew in numbers, I had to increase the hours to accommodate them. The days would start and end in darkness, especially in the short days of winter.

Clients were apt to shift from stable to stable, begging me to follow. "It's just ten minutes farther," they would lie about the extra thirty-kilometre drive.

Eventually, my Fridays all looked the same, starting with a one- or two-hour drive and then navigating among ten to fourteen stables before driving back. My Fridays were rarely shorter than twelve to fourteen hours.

Although I had fun and the clients were warm, engaging, and grateful for the results of chiropractic care for their horses, it was the long drive home that had me questioning my sanity and worrying about orphaning my kids. The last twenty-five kilometres were especially risky as the lack of traffic let me zone out and drive cluelessly in the centre of the two-way roads. A deer, pedestrian, or even an oncoming car would be unlikely to snap me out of my reverie in time for a reflexive life-saving manoeuvre.

I mentioned my concerns to a local client. I had generally been kvetching about the drive to anyone who listened. Sandy suggested I contact a friend of hers, a horse woman who apparently—and remarkably—loved driving. She gave me her friend's number.

The curly haired spunky woman in her late forties came for an interview the next week. She had the husky voice of a smoker, and a brusque no-nonsense attitude. She assured me she didn't smoke cigarettes, and did love driving, was unafraid of long hours, and was indeed very comfortable with horses. I hired her for a two-week trial. It stretched into a ten-year partnership.

Cindy hadn't lied. She didn't smoke cigarettes. She did enjoy her weed and I received an education that had hitherto been restricted to a completely literal belief in "go ask Alice", a fictitious diary of an addicted teen. Cindy could recognize cop cars from the shape and colour of their hub caps. I tended to see a cop car in every car with a roof rack. I was particularly paranoid with Cindy at the wheel. I have a heavy foot and tend to drive 110 km per hour on highways posted with a 90 km per hour limit. Cindy would comfortably cruise at 130.

We picked up three speeding tickets during the first year with Cindy at the helm. I paid half the fine, each time threatening to not do so again.

It always struck me as unfair to saddle her with a cost that exceeded the salary I was paying, however, so I would fork up my half. We either got more effective at spotting cops in the following years, or were luckier, or I reined in Cindy's accelerator somewhat. Either way, we remained ticket free for the following nine years.

About half a year into my employ, Cindy confessed that she had thought the job would be a crazy one. She said she had only accepted because she liked me and liked the idea of working with horses. But chiropractic for horses? Insane! It was clearly a scam to bilk wealthy, credulous horse owners.

One of the first clients Cindy met was a family of three women, a mother and her two adult daughters. They were French, so Cindy had limited comprehension of our rapid French conversations.

She did witness what happened when I started to adjust the older Arab stallion belonging to Mme. Lise Fortier. "Ishmael" had been unable to support himself without leaning on a wall, and had the wobbly ataxic walk of a drunken vagabond. Ishmael had all the classic signs of a wobblers horse, with cervical instability resulting in a lack of proprioceptive balance. Lise's vet had advocated having the horse put down.

Lise's daughter Marie-Claude had a filly, "Cleo", who had been sired by Ishmael. Her back would buckle with light touch and she bucked the moment Marie Claude, at a scant ninety pounds, climbed into the saddle.

After the second adjustment, Ishmael could stand unassisted. By the third and fourth, he was indistinguishable in movement from the healthy horses in the herd. Cleo was rideable after the first adjustment. Marie Claude was grinning ear to ear in reporting the progress. Lise was tearful in her joy. The third Fortier, a younger daughter, Josée, had her horse adjusted prophylactically. She also reported a more-comfortable ride and a greater ease with a left lead canter.

Cindy went from a prosaic sceptic to a full out fan. She noticed that her two horses cocked their tail to the left when she mounted them and immediately grasped the horse and rider connection. She started getting adjusted by Kevin and marvelled that she could now comfortably check her blind spot when driving. I was a little alarmed that she had been unable to do so in the previous months of driving for me. Her horses also stopped canting their tails to the left the moment Kevin restored Cindy's pelvic alignment.

Cindy took on more and more tasks as her understanding grew. She explained where the horses were subluxated to the clients after recording the misalignments I listed as I corrected them. I had a diagram of a horse's spine in the notes I left with the client, and Cindy would circle the areas I had treated, on their forms. She would happily regale the sceptics with her tale of conversion to chiropractic advocate.

That was not the only regaling Cindy would engage in. I started dubbing her propensity to inappropriate comments as her "Tourette's syndrome." Cindy would eye-roll expansively when a very overweight client would wonder out loud how her horse kept getting so back-sore. I would glare behind the client's back and mime a zipped mouth. Cindy was also unabashed about sharing her less-than-enthusiastic views on marriage, men, or sex in general, with anyone and everyone, sometimes reddening the ears of teenage girls who are the regular inhabitants of riding barns.

Cindy was kind-hearted, entertaining, and always flexible and reliable with a crazy schedule of pre-dawn to post-dusk days. She kept me alive and willing to continue with the long hours much longer than I would have on my own.

I suspect many of our clients came to enjoy the repartee and unlikely Mutt-and-Jeff combination we presented. Cindy would gently mock my endless optimism in a cocoon world with my seemingly perfect husband and children, and I'm sure render me a bit more palatable.

Unwilling Equine Patients

THE WOMAN'S VOICE ON THE phone was desperate and breathless. "Is this Dr. Seely? This is Susie here. Do you take on new horse clients? I hate to ask you to come, we are probably two hours or more away from you, but I'll pay whatever extra you want to charge."

Susie described her horse, a previously sweet-tempered gelding, who had morphed into a crazy angry beast. He had apparently kicked her viciously in the last week and had fractured two of her ribs in the process.

Luckily, she was well within the zone I serviced: an area that had expanded to a three-hour radius from my home. I met her at the farm two weeks later.

Susie sported a bandaged wrist as well as the cracked ribs. She peeled back the gauze to show me a nasty wound. "I stupidly let him get close enough to bite me," she explained.

I started to get a bit apprehensive about this patient.

He was pacing in a stall, white eyed and sweaty. A muscled, tattooed man was standing outside the stall. Susie introduced him as Matt, the stable manager and only person willing to handle the cream-coloured gelding called "Bailey", obviously named for his colour, not disposition.

Susie and Matt both then tried to furnish me with the history.

"He's a crazy horse," Matt started. "I think this is stupid. He should

97

be put down!"

"He was a sweet horse," Susie protested. "Something changed this winter."

She said he had been progressing well under saddle and then they gave him the winter off. One day, she arrived and approached him in the field to bring him in for grooming, and he turned his back on her and tried to kick her.

She asked Matt to catch him and he charged at the manager.

"I just got over the fence in time. Crazy mother f—ker was going to trample me. He should be put down I say."

Susie said she couldn't enter the stall anymore, and was scared to be anywhere near him. The new wrist wound had happened when she opened the grid in the stall to put grain in the bucket. He had grazed her wrist with his teeth as she pulled her arm back.

Matt was wearing heavy gloves, so was clearly not indifferent to Bailey's teeth. He also carried a whip in his left hand.

While Matt attached a lead line to the halter, Susie crooned gently to Bailey "Please be good and calm, Bailey. I know you must be hurting."

She remained pressed to the wall on the other side of the breezeway as Matt manoeuvred Bailey into a contraption with four walls. I realized it was a cow stanchion, something I had not seen since vet school.

Matt clicked the hind wall shut behind the sweating horse, effectively neutralizing Bailey's feet as potential weapons. He tied the lead rope to one corner so Bailey had very little reach. It looked cruel and archaic. It meant I could handle Bailey without big risk, but also meant I had very little room to adjust properly. Cindy wisely stayed far away, taking notes, but not volunteering any handling assistance.

I first approached Bailey's thoracic and lumbar spine. I balanced on a stool just outside the stanchion, leaning over to feel his back. He was taut and resistant. I could not assess any subluxations with a back rigid with fear and anger, the paraspinal muscles bulged in their hypertonic state.

I opted instead to move up to his neck.

"Easy, you crazy horse," I breathed into his nose.

I reached up to palpate the cranial cervicalis, the muscle connecting the atlas to the skull. This is the muscle that goes into tetany with headaches and makes people massage the base of their neck, hoping to relieve the pain. Bailey's was a ropy tangled mess. I massaged until he stopped fighting and then thrust at the wings of the atlas. It moved with an audible *thunk*. His eyes visibly softened and both Matt and Susie broke their nervous silence.

Matt muttered "No shit," and Susie let out a nervous giggle.

I released the tight knot on the lead shank so I could adjust both sides of the atlas.

I proceeded to adjust the rest of his spine. He was still taut but not impossible to move.

Matt returned him to the stall after the adjustment, reluctantly conceding that he looked less like a killer, though he wouldn't trust him enough to shed the big gloves or whip.

Susie updated me every few days by e-mail. She reported he was so much calmer that the other boarders had come to the conclusion that she was drugging him senseless. I had scheduled a recheck visit for six weeks later. Two weeks before the date we had agreed on, Susie called to beg for an earlier appointment.

"He's at it again," she said in discouraged tones. "He tried to attack Matt yesterday and his eyes are kind of berserk again."

I managed to get out the following week. Bailey did not greet me like an old friend who had resolved his headache in the past. His eyes showed the white sclera again, and he was pawing at the ground and kicking out at the floorboards at the base of the stall.

Matt led him into the cloister of the stanchion. I found his atlas was again jammed. I adjusted him and was able to get a bit more motion through the rear of his back. Susie paid for the visit, but was visibly less excited than the first time. We had both hoped for a one-time resolution of her changed horse.

On my third and fourth visits, we were all discouraged. Matt was refusing to handle Bailey at all. The pattern was the same. I was greeted by a distrustful Mr. Hyde who morphed into a placid Dr. Jekyll after his atlas was adjusted. I advised Susie that I did not trust Bailey to ever be a trustworthy mount.

"If your husband only beats you when he's drunk, I'd still divorce him when he's sober." I told her. "A horse who tries to kill you when his atlas is awry is not a horse you want. There are too many lovely horses looking for a home to keep trying to rehab Bailey."

She took my advice and bequeathed him to an equine retirement facility where he could live out his life, free of riding obligations. Hopefully, he's not imposing his atlas subluxation killer tendencies on any workers there.

Although it was a rare horse who didn't enjoy my ministrations, there was another notable exception who seemed to have a special hate on for me.

"Jamboree" was not a horse who welcomed affection from people. He barely tolerated John, the man who claimed prime ownership, and kicked John's wife, Ellen, in the shin once. I was happy to not be the only recipient of his antipathy, but I did hold a special spot in his dark heart. He truly hated me.

One day, when I was chatting obliviously with Ellen while adjusting her grey Arab, I walked by the front of Jamboree's stall. Cindy's gasp alerted me, and I moved my head just in time to avoid Jamboree's teeth reaching for my cheek like a rapacious big white shark. He grazed the edge of my cheek and left a saliva trail.

When I adjusted the chestnut gelding, I placed the stool between me and his legs at all times. He was prone to cow kicking, a nasty vice describing an agile manoeuvre allowing a horse to kick out in close proximity and in unexpected directions. Typically, you can assume a horse can only kick toward the rear and that he needs a couple feet of leverage to deliver an effective kick. All novice riders are taught to stay close to a horse's rump when passing behind, and to reassure the horse with a hand on his back to avoid being kicked. That assumes a steed who is only kicking in fear and flight. A horse who is maliciously out to deliver a kick is a different beast.

Even John was not spared Jamboree's malevolence. On one occasion when John was driving him, the gelding elected to charge between a tractor and a barn, crashing and overturning the sulky in the process.

John and Ellen were a gracious older couple who loved their three horses equally, much as good parents don't favour obedient children over the problem child. Cindy and I invariably carved extra time out of our schedule to have tea and biscuits in a house that looked and felt magically transported out of rural England and plunked into the middle of Ontario.

The pleasure of their company and the knowledge that Jamboree did perform better with adjustments kept me risking my life and limb every two months. Ellen had two other horses who adjusted comfortably and with good results.

I had many other horses that clients anticipated would be dangerous patients. I arrived at one barn and was greeted with a crowd of around twelve people. They watched breathlessly as I adjusted a big Welsh cob. I was cautioned that he was apt to explode when his neck was touched.

The crowd drifted away, I suspect more disappointed than impressed, when he stood placidly for the treatment once his atlas was adjusted.

Another horse, "Han Solo", had fractured several ribs of a massage therapist, and had pinned an osteopath against the wall prior to my first visit.

Again, fireworks were anticipated. The stable owner wanted me to refuse "Hans" as a patient. She was a big fan of the work I did with her school horses and had no vested curiosity in seeing me broken. Hans tolerated the treatment admirably. He was never the most huggable of horses, but his owner, Joan, swore I was one of his favourite people and that he was generally mellow for weeks after his adjustment. I was always very quick in identifying and immediately adjusting a misplaced vertebra. I suspected Hans would be intolerant of any hesitant palpation.

When I hired a locum to run my practice while our family took a two-month mini sabbatical in Australia, Joan voted to forgo any adjustments. Hans had laid his ears flat and started snorting as my substitute motion-palpated his spine. Joan was not eager for a recurrence of the injuries Hans had visited on his first two therapists. They waited for my return.

Paralysis and Paresis

"HEIDI" LOOKED AT ME WITH big brown doleful eyes. She was wrapped in a quilt which I would have proudly put on a guest bed: hand-sewn in vibrant colours, clearly a labour of hours of love. Her owner, Joan, had equally plaintive brown eyes.

"Is there anything you can do?" she pleaded. "I don't mind the cost. And I refuse to put her down. I think she's happy enough in the cart, but it kills me to see her paralyzed when she's a dog who lives for her daily walk."

Heidi was a handsome and slightly obese Basset Hound with the droopy ears and eyes that belied any claims of being happy. Golden Retrievers look happy. Bassets look like they would like to discuss the existential darkness of the world while curled next to the fire. I doubted she was ever a keen exerciser.

As Joan recounted her history, my heart sank. Heidi had been paralyzed in the back end for more than five months. Although Joan had been willing to fork up the $7,000 or so for an MRI and disc surgery, the neurologist had refused to do the surgery when Heidi had not responded to toe pinching.

We are taught in third year vet school that there is little likelihood of a good surgical outcome if there is no evidence of deep pain.

Bassets and Dachshunds are sadly over represented in an animal chiropractor's waiting room. The discs sandwiched between the vertebrae are genetically chaotically arranged in these long-backed, short-legged breeds. The discs are very vulnerable to herniation where the gelatinous centre bulges out like a flattened jelly doughnut and exerts pressure on the spinal cord. The result is a sad-looking dog in need of a good wheelchair. This is so common, in fact, that a mobile cart has been concocted for them. And many a neurosurgeon's kitchen upgrades have been funded by the pricey surgery a discectomy commands.

We were sternly admonished to be wary of disc cases in the animal chiropractic course. "Adjust above and below, but never at the site of the herniated disc," we were cautioned. Every owner of a paralyzed dog who came seeking help, however, was just as frantic and motivated as Joan. Most were opting for a non-surgical route because the surgery would involve a choice between paying the mortgage and groceries, versus the comfort of their pet. And each time I palpated, an aberrant spinous process sat there just begging to be adjusted. As my practice grew, I figure I was seeing a minimum of one paralyzed or unstable disc case weekly.

Contrary to the pessimism expressed in the notes from the animal chiropractic course in Moline, most disc cases would improve dramatically. Few scenarios are as exciting as having a flaccid paralysis reverse under your hands. Owners were weepy with happiness.

And the staff at the front desk got to see first hand what chiropractic can accomplish. Many of my clients were perhaps weirder and more demanding than the regular clients and, as a result, the front staff usually had a tougher job on my afternoons. I was always happy when the staff was party to seeing the seeming miracle of a dog who was carried into the room come trotting out some ten minutes later. It made the onerous task of working on my busy shift afternoons a little more tolerable for the valiant team in the front office.

Not all paralyzed patients responded. I had one notable llama who was carted to the clinic in a trailer weekly for three visits, to the delight of staff and children in the waiting room. The first visit seemed to restore some strength and allow her to lift her head to eat, which motivated the second two visits. She never regained use of her hind legs, and sadly was euthanized. I never knew whether a disc or tumour was the culprit.

Other dogs would sometimes improve and then plateau at a certain level of paresis or weakness. They would often be brought in with the cart, which would allow them full mobility so they could walk with their owners and conduct relatively normal lives. Adjustments would usually relieve the stresses triggered from being kept in a harness. Typically, the herniated site itself rarely presented as a source of chronic pain.

Heidi was my first patient who had been refused surgery due to her poor prognosis. I was not optimistic for any restoration of strength. I did think I could help relieve some discomfort Heidi was experiencing from spending hours in the harness.

Joan was more hopeful. She had met an owner of a paralyzed Dachshund who I had adjusted and witnessed him bounding comfortably in the leash-free dog park. She had then Googled my name and read several other accounts of paralyzed-to-walking stories. These tend to be the loudest and most laudatory reviews. Lacklustre results don't seem to motivate online testimonials. So Joan was not in any way discouraged by my admonishment that Heidi would be more comfortable, but unlikely to walk again.

I palpated Heidi's spine. She was a chiropractic mess—unsurprising after spending most of the past half year in a metal contraption that restricted motion in the trunk and allowed only limited head motion. She didn't seem in any distress when I adjusted four contiguous vertebrae in her lower thorax that were all positioned aberrantly. I scheduled a recheck for the following Tuesday,

On the subsequent visit, Joan swore that Heidi struck her as happier, and that she almost seemed to paddle occasionally, with her hind legs scratching on the hardwood floor. I didn't even report that in my notes as it seemed the product of hope, not science. I did note that the owner was pleased with the dog's progress.

There was nothing equivocal about Heidi's improvement on the following visit. Joan arrived wreathed in smiles and had her ten-year-old granddaughter on the other end of Heidi's leash.

"Take the harness off for Dr. Seely, Leah," Joan commanded the girl while they were still seated in the waiting room.

Leah unclipped the harness and let it drop to the ground.

"Come here, sweetie," Joan crooned.

And Heidi ran forward. There was no unsteadiness in her gait. A human trapped in a wheelchair for six months would have staggered and likely used a walker to support weakened legs. But Heidi ran like she had been malingering for months, and practising leg squats nightly.

The front staff and I applauded.

One of the receptionists started bringing her dog in for care the next week. Her dog was asymptomatic, but she wanted a piece of the action. I agreed to see her dog monthly, just prophylactically.

Heidi remained under care for the remaining eight years of her life, sometimes monthly, and sometimes every eight to twelve weeks. Joan said she knew Heidi needed adjusting when her gait sounded arrhythmic on the hardwood floor.

The cart remained dusty and unused until it was donated to an animal shelter.

Ironman

MARY CALLED ME AT HOME late one evening. I answered because calls on our home line after 6 PM were invariably family calls. I was wrong this time. I recognized Mary's strident husky tones immediately. Mary was a regular horse client I saw once a month when I visited Almonte, a community over a hundred kilometres away.

"I need you to see Benny this week. He's walking funny. You know what a brilliant stud he is. He's supposed to be vetted next week and should get at least a hundred and twenty thousand, which is probably still a steal! But that won't happen if he walks the way he did today."

"Mary, I don't know how I can do that," I prevaricated. "I'm on holiday next week. I fly to BC the day after tomorrow."

"No worries, Dr. Seely, I'll bring him to you tomorrow." Mary clearly was not going to accept a no.

I gave Mary the directions to the house.

Kevin looked at me askance when I hung up the phone. "Really?" He was incredulous. "You are going to adjust a horse here tomorrow? You know my parents are coming. And we still have to pack."

We were both a little on edge. We were about to head out to British Columbia for more than a relaxing holiday. We were registered in the Canadian Ironman, a race held in Penticton. We'd been training diligently for over one year, as much as that is possible while working forty-plus hours a week.

The Ironman is a crazy event, a one day long triathlon. It was the chimera of three endurance events, combining the courses of the Waikiki Rough Water Swim (2.4 miles), the Around-Oahu Bike Race (112 miles, originally over two days), and the Honolulu Marathon (26.2 miles) in Hawaii in 1978. I heard about the challenging event in the '80s, but couldn't fathom the training and fitness level required to finish one. Kevin and I participated in a number of shorter triathlons in our pre-children phase of life. The Ironman sat as a distant goal.

"When I turn forty," I vowed. "I'll do an Ironman."

On the morning of my fortieth birthday, I found Kevin diligently Googling the entry requirements. It was my first indication that Kevin was keen to join me. It proved a wise move. The amount of training required is reputed to create Ironman Widows and Widowers when only one half of a couple is training. I suspect Ironman Divorcees is a logical sequela.

Kev and I loved the training. We termed our long bike rides "Tours of Tim Hortons", and would explore different routes near our home, stopping to replenish calories with coffees, soups, and pastries at Tim Hortons. The Thursdays we had carved out as couple's time while the kids were in school served as the bulk of our bike training. We were able to mass up to two-hundred-kilometre bike rides between the hours the school bus picked them up, and before the school bus dropped them off at the end of our lane. We squeezed in long runs and swims in the early mornings, and took turns parenting when the other trained. It was generally lots of fun.

As the race loomed, our only criterion was getting to the starting line rested and injury free. The race has a seventeen-hour time restriction. If you don't cross the line in under seventeen hours, you are not deemed an Ironman, and the race officials ask you to leave the course. I was very worried about the timing.

Kevin was more optimistic. His mantra was "No stinking glow lights!" If you finish the race in the dark, you must wear a glowing necklace that the race officials hand out at sundown. Kev was determined to be finished before dark.

The day before flying was a typical flurry of last-minute packing, as well as hosting Kevin's parents for supper. It was not surprising that Kevin was not a fan of my adding a chiropractic horse appointment to the chaos of the day.

Mary and her husband drove up at dusk, a good hour after the time Mary had scheduled. The table was laid and a lasagna was bubbling in the oven. I left Kevin and my mother-in-law, Jane, in charge of stalling dinner.

My father-in-law, John, accompanied me outside. John was excited about witnessing a chiropractic treatment of a horse. He planted himself off to the side, in the field, with his video camera, hoping to film the action.

The horse trailer was violently lurching when the truck pulled into the field. Loud metallic thuds were emanating from the trailer.

Mary grimaced. "This is Benny's first time in a trailer. He's not very happy. It took us over two hours to load him. That's why we're so late."

Mary unclipped the back door. Benny's back was dripping in sweat. She entered the front of the trailer and undid the knot of the lead rope. She backed Benny out of the truck.

Benny spun wildly around Mary as she held onto him by the lead rope.

Mary's husband offered to help but she told him sharply to just stay in the truck.

"Benny's very nervous," she said. "I think anyone other than me is just going to freak him out more. Get your stool, Dr. Seely. We need to get this done before the storm hits and really gets Benny upset."

The sky was darkening ominously. Low rumblings of thunder were sounding at regular intervals.

OK. I was fully nervous now.

I announced, "I have never been kicked before, Mary. And today would really be a bad day for me to be kicked with my Ironman race this weekend."

I still don't know what made me announce that. Of course, it was prescient. In the next minute, a clap of thunder sounded, John turned his camera on with a metallic click, and Mary rebuked Benny for raising his head. It all happened simultaneously. Benny reared up on his hind legs and I felt a sharp thwack to my head and saw the proverbial stars. Benny had clipped my forehead with his front hoof.

"Did he hit you? He didn't, did he?" asked Mary. It had happened so fast she had not witnessed it.

Sadly, John didn't get the footage. He worried that the click of the camera had triggered the rear. He moved to the safety of the porch for the remainder of the treatment.

Benny settled and I was able to adjust him, though I did all the adjustments from the ground, not trusting Benny to not explode with the addition of a stool.

I reassured everyone that I felt fine, ignoring the throbbing of my temple. I kept touching my head, expecting to feel blood trickling down.

When Mary and her husband drove away, I could finally examine my face in the bathroom mirror. No blood, just a clean crescent mark from the horseshoe. It faded in a couple of days. I wasn't hurt or concussed. I was very lucky in either being a perfect distance from the hoof, or Benny carefully avoided hurting me.

Benny went on to pass the vetting with flying colours. Mary elected not to sell him, hoping to keep him intact as a lucrative stud.

***

Kevin and I were able to fly out the next day to Penticton to race our first Ironman. My parents flew out to support us and take care of our children.

Kev finished comfortably in the light of the day in eleven hours and forty minutes. I finished ten minutes later. The time gap allowed the kids to link hands with Kevin and break the finish ribbon with him, and then circle back to do the same with me.

The sky is noticeably darker in my finish photo, arguably dusk. But I, too, was able to finish the race with "No stinking glow stick."

Have Hands Will Travel

OUR FAMILY HAS A THING for Jack Reacher. The romance of being able to travel unencumbered with a folding toothbrush in a pocket and a credit card to replace clothes when they are too smelly or unserviceable is just so tempting.

I achieve that more than the rest of my family, sometimes to great inconvenience. When we were once visiting Kev's brother in Vermont, Savannah got her pants wet running through wet grass. When my sister-in-law Cindy suggested she go change, Sav admitted "I'm not sure if I have a second pair, Aunt Cindy. If Dad packed, then maybe? But if Mom packed, then I doubt it. She is known to pack 'light'."

I had the same urges with my profession. Veterinary offices are pricey to outfit, and expensive to run. When I embraced chiropractic, my mobile office became a minimalist's dream. It consisted of a $12 folding stepstool from Canadian Tire, and a clipboard for my notes. Farmers would hasten to my car door, offering to help carry all my stuff, and be surprised by my spartan tools.

All I really needed was my hands. I have used a bale of hay, a fence post, or a tractor seat to get the necessary leverage to adjust a horse. And for a dog, the ten fingers suffice. It meant I could offer up chiropractic help for animals in unexpected places with zero preparation.

This proved to be a boon in our travels. When Savannah was debating university choices, we opted to tour the Maritime provinces, visiting universities in a rented camper van. We became less rigorous in our university explorations when Sav fell in love with our old Alma Mater, Acadia. Rather than take a campus tour of St Francis Xavier in Nova Scotia, we opted to visit an old classmate and roommate from our university years, Macky. Macky lived in a beautiful summer cottage on the Bay of Fundy.

Our teens disappeared in an unusual display of quick friendship with Macky's two boys. They built a campfire on the beach and swam in the moonlight in a magical show of bioluminescence with little diatoms emitting eerie light when they were disturbed, leaving a body silhouette alight to mark the passage of the swimmers.

We reconnected with Macky, and Kevin and Macky resurrected their acoustic guitar skills, playing songs from the '80s on the front porch, with rusty fingers and poorly practised voices.

While Kev and Macky rehashed old songs, I wandered down to the beach and spent some time making friends with Macky's big lumbering older lab, "Finn". I was surprised that Finn didn't follow me up to the house.

"I take it Finn is not a fan of country and western?" I joked.

"Ah, Finn is a sad old dog," Macky explained. "She hasn't been able to do stairs for probably three or four years now. It's hard on her here. In the city, she copes just fine. We have a bungalow there."

I climbed down the long wooden set of stairs to the beach again.

Finn rose to greet me. She stoically tolerated my fingers probing the length of her spine. Sure enough, she had very little appreciable motion in the sacrum and her lower lumbar. The sacrum was tilted in such a way that her tail was tucked between her legs awkwardly. I should have noticed the tail carriage earlier. Her greeting of us had looked nervous and a bit aggressive, with the tail tucked tightly between her hind legs. I adjusted her. The wine I had guzzled at supper made me forget the niceties of asking permission first.

We slept in the camper while the kids afforded us a little privacy by sleeping in the house with their new friends. When we entered to share the marvellous breakfast Macky and his wife had prepared, we were surprised by a wet-snouted, enthusiastic Finn, tail wagging vigorously.

Mary, Macky's wife, was befuddled. "Finn always sleeps on the beach, but came up last night and jumped on our bed. Wretched sandy beast! She hasn't done that in years. I can't quite figure it out."

"Hmm. How much do you hate the sand in the bed?" I asked. "'Cause I should probably 'fess up. I adjusted her last night."

They claimed to be thrilled. Their teenage boys were believable in their gratitude. Macky said it was the nicest gift we could have brought them.

Usually, it's Kevin's hands that make us welcome visitors, often at the expense of Kevin's holidays when he is called on to adjust the hosts repeatedly. This time it felt good to be able to offer my own "hostess gift".

Opinionated Animals

"BARNEY" WAS ANOTHER DOG I adjusted as a thank you to friends. Kevin and I had met Pam and Hondo when I was ballooned with a seven-month Forest in the making.

We could not source a local midwife, and were referred to a midwife based in Huntsville, four hours from home. Rosemary was a caricature of a midwife with hair long enough to sit on, thin, plain speaking, and living in an off-the-grid log house with earthenware and herbal teas.

She invited us for a "meet and greet" and physical exam, and set us up with an equally pregnant client, Pam, who ran a local bed and breakfast.

Kev and I warmed to Pam and Hondo immediately. The house was overrun with cats, Pam's art, and Hondo's photographs of their world travels. Savannah was two at the time and was charmed by Pam's two-year-old son who ruled the house and covered the living room with his toys. It was not a bed and breakfast to woo a middle-aged inflexible traveler, but was perfect for our casual parenting style.

We visited several times through the last stages of our pregnancies, and each went on to have an uncomplicated home delivery.

The four-hour drive proved a challenge for Forest's impatient two-hour labour. Rosemary arrived long after his birth which was attended by Allison, a seasoned Ottawa-based midwife from England who was technically a student midwife, as she sought to gain her Ontario credentials. Rosemary signed the appropriate forms, measured Forest and weighed him, and ensured the birth was properly registered.

I gather the birth of Pam's daughter was more traditionally timed.

We sent news of our mutually successful deliveries, with the birth-days separated by two days, and didn't see Pam and Hondo for years.

Years later, we were again visitors to the Muskoka area. Savannah had been introduced to Camp Tawingo by her cousin Aidan. Even though the camp reiterated much of the highlights of home—a lake, canoeing, songs around campfires, and no television—Savannah was hooked. It was a social Mecca and fraught with unique camp challenges, badges, slogans, and songs that generated generations of loyal camp graduates. Savannah persuaded the boys, and best friend Kiki, to sign up. The camp remains one of the highlights of their childhood.

Visitors day was a carefully orchestrated event where you could pick up the kids for seven hours before returning them to a celebratory campers-only evening once the parents were exiled. Huntsville would bulge at the seams as parents booked children in for pizza lunches, and then congregate in droves at The Nutty Chocolatier, a candy store worthy of Hogsmead fame.

Huntsville was too far from home to negotiate a proper visit in one day. We searched the Internet and found Pam and Hondo's Bed & Breakfast to be a flourishing business. We stayed in the room we had stayed in twelve years previously. The bed had been upgraded, but the claw-foot bathtub was just as quaint, and the food possibly even better than we remembered.

I adjusted Pam's horses before leaving, and Kev adjusted Pam and Hondo. It was the beginning of several visits as we came to love the area, enjoy trading stories with Pam and Hondo, and especially returning for Pam's baking and hospitality.

Years later, when Forest and Pam's daughter were both teenagers, we increased our annual visits to Huntsville for a second reason. The town had become home to Ironman 70.3 Muskoka, an epic race with hills, winds, cold water, and boasting rights as a longer-than-standard bike course for the Half Ironman distance race. Kev and I decided it would be a lovely pre-Ironman tune up for the full distance race in Lake Placid.

Pam woke us with a 4:00-AM breakfast and drove us to the start line. We were cheered on in the swim segment by Hondo providing volunteer guarding duties on a paddle board, and then given refreshments by Pam and her two kids at an aid table. The family gamely volunteered at the event yearly.

The following morning, we had a final breakfast before driving home.

"Barney" held court in the family kitchen, and I scratched him gently behind the ears. Barney was the house Labrador Retriever. He was a sleepy, older, affectionate dog, always wagging his tail to greet the multitude of strangers who kept invading his house. His domain was the kitchen. He was a prolific shedder and Pam neither wanted the hair nor the allergen potential to invade the whole house. He was allowed in the hardwood-floored kitchen and the front porch. The rest of the house was off limits.

When I saw Barney awkwardly getting to his feet, legs splaying on the slippery surface, I offered to adjust him. Pam accepted with alacrity. She was a staunch chiropractic patient, always especially eager for our visits as she loved Kevin's confident hands. She no longer had horses at the farm, and I was happy to find another way of expressing my gratitude for the discounted prices and warm welcome we always received at the farmhouse.

Barney thanked me with a wet lick. It was his first adjustment and he did seem to move more comfortably that day.

One year later, Kevin and I returned to race Ironman 70.3 Muskoka again. This time we were warming up for Ironman Mont Tremblant in August. The hills were a welcome training ground for the climbing anticipated in the Laurentian race.

We arrived in the evening and Hondo greeted us with a beer in the front porch.

Suddenly, Hondo exclaimed "What the hell?"

A big hairy bum was nudging my beer aside as Barney's warm buttocks sidled backwards between my thighs.

Pam followed from the living room. "You bad dog, Barney!" she exclaimed. "Sorry, Ali. I don't know what got into him. He just marched through the house. He's never done that! He knows he isn't allowed in the living room!"

Barney was leaning into me, so clearly inviting an adjustment. I leaned in and thrust on the subluxated sacrum which Barney was proffering.

"I think Barney remembers my last visit," I said.

I continued to adjust Barney, once a year, and always with an enormous welcome, until he passed of old age.

It turns out dogs can quite easily rival elephants with their good memories.

Marathon
Misadventure

THE LAST TUESDAY IN APRIL had client files piling up at the Carp Road Animal Hospital. The waiting room was packed, but I was hard pressed to rush any of my clients. Everyone seemed to want to let me know they were thrilled I was alive. I felt a little bit like I was attending my own funeral. I had not narrowly escaped death, but being within two hundred metres of a bomb, and eight minutes from being directly in its zone of detonation, qualified me to most of my friends as a miracle. Many people had done the math, depriving me of my eight minutes and calculated that I was likely a victim of the bomb. For a couple hours or days, they assumed I might be wounded or dead.

I had qualified for Boston three times before 2013. Each qualifying time seemed to be a harbinger of my fertility and I would go on to conceive a baby instead of racing. The time I posted two weeks before conceiving Savannah remains my fastest at 3:28. I got slower in the following years but, luckily, so does the Boston qualifying time.

Kevin and I had wanted to race together, but the required limit for women is much more achievable than the male one. I needed a 3:45, and Kevin a 3:15. That would take healthy hamstrings, and no full-time job and parenting for Kevin. When I qualified in 2012, Kev said he would be delighted to come as a support crew.

The race was magnificent. I have never seen a more supportive crowd. The entire race was littered with water cups, because between each water station were children, students, and Bostonians offering juice, popsicles, water, kisses, and encouragement.

I had decorated my face with temporary Canadian maple leaf tattoos. This garnered lots of "GO Canada!" to egg me on. I also befriended Canadians along the way who would sidle up and run with me when they saw my red and white cheeks.

Kev positioned himself at the twenty-three-mile mark. We had previously tried to meet at the finish line of races and have learned that this is a hopeless exercise. The crowds often prevent you from seeing the actual finish, and you hover there, long after the predicted time, hoping it means you have missed them, and not that the race went horribly poorly for them. When you do finally meet up, the runner is motivated to leave earlier than they want, forgoing massage and extra food, just wanting to put the support crew out of their bored misery. We know this well because we've travelled that route. We wisely decided that I could wend my way back to the hotel with public transport after the race, and that Kev would cheer me on from a less-crowded mile marker.

Mile 23 was a perfect choice. I could see Kev from a block away. We hugged and kissed. Only three miles to go.

I finished in 3:54. It was a full twenty-two minutes slower than my qualifying time, but was a minute faster than the time I needed to qualify for the following Boston.

I was very happy. My training had been typical of a Canadian winter: lots of indoor bike sessions, cross country skiing, and the odd slow slushy run. I had estimated that I would finish in 4:15. I had announced that to my clients, friends, and family. Secretly, I hoped to finish under 3:55, but only Kev was privy to that goal. There is no anonymity in running races anymore. You can be tracked at every kilometre. I always prefer to minimize expectations and exceed them rather than not achieve loftier declared ones.

I high-fived the teens who were handing out medals, accepted my finisher medal and space blanket, and grabbed a bagel. I was ushered by volunteers to the vans, which stored our dry clothes. Around eight minutes after I had crossed the tape, I grabbed my clothes and hobbled over to a lamp post so I could lever my legs into sweats without sitting down. The risk of sitting is that you can't get up!

I was threading one leg into the sweats when a large bang startled the chatter of the large group of marathoners surrounding me.

"Ouch," I complained, holding my ears. "That is a rude time to fire off a cannon."

The girl beside me nodded her agreement. She was distractedly dialling her cell phone. "Yeah," she said. "That friggin' hurt. I'm trying to find out where my friend is. We ran together until Mile 20 and then she wanted to walk out a cramp. She should be here by now though."

A second cannon shot ran out again.

"Wow. Glad I'm not closer. That is pretty deafening."

The girl didn't respond. She had the phone glued closely to her ear.

"Holy shit." She pressed the disconnect. "That was my friend Emma. She says they were stopped and aren't allowed to finish their race. She's like crying, she's so disappointed. It makes no sense. I guess there was some sort of explosion?"

I finished dressing and started walking toward the finish line.

A policeman stood in the path and turned everyone away. "Sorry folks. This way is closed. You'll have to find another way back." He looked pretty serious and wasn't allowing any questions.

I walked with the mass of disgruntled runners. People were grumbling about missing linking up with their family, or finding their cars. I knew I just had to find a subway station and figured there should be one south of Copley, the one I had intended to take.

Fifteen shuffling minutes later, I saw the subway logo. I walked down the stairs and was greeted by a policewoman rolling out the metal mesh gate.

"Sorry guys, this station is closed." A large crowd of runners were congregating at the foot of the stairs.

"Was it a bomb?" a voice rang out. "My wife says they are reporting that it was a bomb!"

The policewoman was implacable. "I can't comment yet, I'm afraid".

The crowd dispersed and I continued to walk south. I had no knowledge of the city whatsoever, but figured if I continued in a straight line, I might find another station. It was good planning. I did find another station after around a half hour of walking, but it too was closed.

All around me were people walking dazedly, all glued to their phones. I asked another blanketed runner if I could borrow her phone to call my husband.

Kev answered right away.

"Congrats. You qualified for next year's Boston," he announced. "You looked awesome when I saw you. I'm just trying to hunt down a race that I can qualify at. I'd like to do this next year with you."

"Kev. They say there may have been a bomb," I interrupted him. "I'm not having any luck with finding a subway station that's open. I think I'll try to get over the river and try there. Or maybe grab a taxi."

"A bomb? Are you serious? Crazy! Yes. Grab a taxi and get back to the hotel. Soon."

I kept walking. I saw a couple of runners shivering in shorts and tanks. The day had been cool and windy, ideal for running, but brutally cold when the sweat congealed. They told me they'd been unable to get to the clothes when they were turned around before finishing the race. I gave them my blanket and mittens.

The sound of sirens was a constant background noise. Fire trucks, ambulances, and police cars whizzed by on otherwise fairly quiet streets.

I gave up on finding transportation. There was clearly none to be found. I crossed the river and started following it east. The hotel overlooked the river, I was bound to run into it eventually. Three hours later,

I walked into our hotel room.

Kev has been busy at the computer. It seems everyone had believed my pessimistic time prediction and that timing would have landed me squarely at the finish line when the bombs detonated. Kev was madly putting out fires of concern from family, clients, and friends. My habit of not carrying a cell phone was being roundly cursed.

I learned later that Forest had been in a lifeguard course at our local pool and had been taken aside to be told about the bombing. It was only around an hour later when Sue, the instructor, learned that I was unscathed. Hearing that my unflappable son almost cried publicly at that news was likely my most emotional moment. Luckily, Savannah just assumed I finished ahead of the bomb, and Logan learned about the bomb and my safe status simultaneously.

Three people died and three hundred and sixty-four people were injured due to the two handmade bombs that day. Although people marvelled that I was unhurt despite being so close, I am more grateful about the Mile 23 plan Kev and I had concocted that pre-empted his being at the finish line. It was the supporting friends and families of the runners and the volunteers who made up the bulk of the injured that day. I was so grateful that Kevin wasn't among them.

We flew home and managed to avoid the throngs of reporters interviewing the passengers who were clearly runners. I tucked my medal and finisher's shirt deep inside my suitcase. When I was invited to run a support run in Renfrew with other local racers the following week, I brought my dog, "Haka", along. Having a hundred and thirty pounds of loyal, loving, canine companion helped a group run feel safe.

The following Tuesday, I experienced the overwhelming reception of sixty-plus people who had been convinced I had almost died, with hugs, tears, and warnings about the risks of being without a phone. I felt like an imposter. I hadn't been so close to death. But it was a wonderful validation of being appreciated.

The Russian

"THIS ONE SHOULD BE INTERESTING," Mary, one of the clinic receptionists, announced ominously when she came to retrieve me from the staff room. My shift was usually six uninterrupted hours, so I would retreat to the staff room for cookies-and-coffee sustenance whenever there was a short gap between patients.

I followed her out to the front reception. A very scrawny man sat with a Dachshund mixed-breed dog in his lap, swaddled in a blanket. The man wore a tank top and his arms were covered in colourful tattoos of snakes and naked women. He was stifling sobs. A young boy was looking at him with curiosity as his mother attempted to ignore the scene while they awaited their appointment with another doctor.

I ushered the man into the privacy of an exam room. He introduced himself as Roloff.

"My frrriend Vana, she say you feex her dog. You make her dog walk. My dog, he need you to feex him, *da*?"

He was heavily accented. Vana was a lovely Russian woman whose Beagle had been paretic when I met him. She was ecstatic when he started walking after three treatments. She hugged me at every visit, exclaiming how "heppy" her family was to have "Egor" walking again.

"I certainly hope to be able to help your dog," I assured Roloff. "But discs are tricky. It may be that your dog needs surgery."

I explained the nature of disc herniations and how it was difficult to assess how much cord damage had been sustained without seeing a myelogram or CT scan.

Roloff's eyes were glazing over as I spoke.

I stopped to check if he was understanding my typically rapid-fire English.

"*Da, da.* I understand," he assured me. "But I have no money. Vana, she say this work."

I adjusted his dog, "Misha", a sweet-tempered mixed breed with an unfortunate genetic legacy of the long back and short legs of a Dachshund, and the curly hair and molten brown eyes of another, unidentifiable, breed. Misha had no reflexes or movement in his hind legs, but could respond to a pinch test and had good anal tone. I told Roloff I was cautiously optimistic. We scheduled a visit the following week.

Roloff was much cheerier on his second visit. Misha was apparently moving his back legs when he slept, and was trying to pull himself along the floor with some spastic motions of the hind legs. It was easier to communicate with Roloff when he wasn't holding back tears.

"It is good Misha is better," he announced. "I no go to jail if Misha no walk."

"Prison?" I asked, not sure if I had understood.

"*Da!*" Roloff answered. He explained that he had been a drug mule, somehow by accident, and had been sentenced to eight months in jail. He told me it was fine and deserved, but he couldn't leave Misha in this state with a friend. "When he walk, and pee, and poo, then good. I leave him with friend. Police, they understand," he assured me.

I was pretty naive about the underpinnings of the Law, but found it unlikely that they would wait to incarcerate Roloff until he was secure about the future of his dog. I asked him about it on each visit, convinced I was being spun a tale.

When Roloff brought Misha in for his fifth adjustment, he was jubilant. "Misha sort of walk to road yesterday. He pee—like a girl—but he pee!"

Roloff had been expressing Misha's bladder by hand, gently pressing on his abdomen to release the stream, so this was huge progress.

I started quizzing Roloff about his childhood in Russia. He was animated in his descriptions, always choppy with his verb tenses, and prone to throwing in Russian words, but very willing to talk about Leningrad. I asked about the myth of lining up for bread. He told me his family would take turns subbing in for his mother for forty-eight-hour waits for a loaf of bread.

"This country beautiful and so lucky." He never sounded remotely resentful about the drug sting he described he'd been caught up in. "I stupid," he explained. "My truck use for carry drugs. I never check. I now know, stupid! Jail is fair! When Misha good …"

When Misha could walk, Roloff hugged me. He scheduled the appointment for the following week. "He walk, but no run. He need you more, I think."

The following week, Misha was a no show. I asked Mary to call Roloff. She reported that the phone was disconnected.

Vana confirmed several weeks later that Roloff was indeed serving his sentence, and that the authorities had allowed him compassionate stay until he could comfortably leave Misha in the care of a friend. I can only hope and assume that Misha was comfortably ambulatory, and that Roloff was reassured as he served his time in a penitentiary.

The CVO Complaint

I TOOK MY HIPPOCRATIC OATH seriously. I was determined to do no harm. That got me in lots of hot water when I worked as an associate. I refused to declaw cats, euthanize healthy or mildly ill animals, and I would always try to find an affordable option when money stood in the way of helping a patient. The conflict between animal needs and client wants became completely nullified when I shifted to an animal chiropractic practice. The cost was low and consistent. The client was self-selected in being motivated to alleviate suffering. I loved my unambiguous role.

I felt I should be impervious to client complaints. Veterinarians are governed by the College of Veterinarians of Ontario, the CVO. We pay for and maintain the organization, but it is not our ally. The CVO represents the public and ensures that a standard of practice, both ethical and professional, is maintained. A letter from the CVO triggers the heart palpitations and cold sweat skin akin to seeing police sirens in the rear-view mirror. It means someone is pretty upset with you as a vet. Penalties range from no action to heavy fines and loss of license.

One fateful day, I received such an envelope at work. It was the first indication that I had an aggrieved client. When I opened the letter, it went from bad to worse. I learned that a cat I had seen months earlier had apparently died due to my actions.

The information was initially very scant. The Office Manager, Brenda, was asked to furnish my notes on the client interaction. Brenda allowed me to read the notes in her presence. I then remembered the encounter.

Mrs. and Mr. Fields had brought "Smudge" to the clinic. Smudge was a heavy, older, but not geriatric, cat. She had been acutely sore and roached. The Fields were cat-sitting for their daughter who lived in Toronto but was away on a two-month business trip. I remembered the Fields because I had been asked to squeeze them in between other appointments. My colleague Shari had been initially booked to see the cat.

Shari had cornered me between appointments to ask that I see Smudge. She said they were adamant that the cat needed chiro, but had been told a regular veterinary exam was necessary for a non-client appointment. Shari had concurred that Smudge's back seemed to be the problem.

She advised them to get the cat adjusted and that a painkiller would help because Smudge seemed to be in such distress.

I examined Smudge and adjusted her. I tabled the adjustments meticulously in the notes. As I was leaving the room, the Fields advised me that they would be returning Smudge to their daughter in Toronto that weekend and would be unable to schedule a follow up.

Mrs. Fields said "The other doctor said we should give her a painkiller too. What do you think?"

I assured her I would confer with Shari, but that it seemed like a wise course of action. Shari and I met at the breezeway between appointment rooms and agreed on a short course of Metacam for the cat.

Drugs in veterinary medicine are a tricky thing. So many of the medications are derived from being used in humans. If sufficient tests are run for an animal patient, and the drug can prove to be lucrative in that species, the drug will have an animal formulation. Many times, this is not the case. Drugs are then deemed "off-label". Metacam was licensed for dogs, and was "off-label" but commonly prescribed for cats. Our options for pain control in cats at the time were very limited.

That was the end of my notes and memory of Smudge. As far as I knew, she was happily in Toronto with the Fields' daughter. I sent off the notes to the CVO, curious but also trepidatious to hear the actual denouement.

The CVO did not keep me in suspense for long. I was allowed to see a copy of the formal Letter of Complaint.

It turns out that Smudge had left the office, comfortable, stretching, and pretty much her old self. They report having felt ambivalent about giving the oral medicine at that point, but figured the veterinarians knew best. They gave the Metacam for three days as prescribed. By the second day, Smudge was back at home in Toronto with their daughter, but seemed lethargic. By day three, Smudge was vomiting and no longer eating. The daughter took Smudge to her regular veterinarian. She was diagnosed as being in end stage renal failure. After a week on IV fluids, she was euthanized.

I felt sick. I double checked the records and my math, but the dosage was conservative. There were suggestions in the literature that Metacam, like any non-steroidal anti-inflammatory medication, could be nephrotoxic, causing damage to kidney cells. Both Shari and I were named in the complaint. I was the one who had written the script, however. I felt hugely sad and culpable.

The letter from the CVO advocated against communicating with the client. My office said the same. I sent a letter of apology immediately, regardless.

Then I waited. It was eight months of cankers, many sleepless nights and a nasty gnawing feeling that I was hard pressed to identify, but was never really gone. I'm not sure how people deal with bigger issues: tax fraud, affairs, lies. This one investigation, and the knowledge that I had been implicated in a death, was all encompassing.

I was approached by the makers of Metacam, who offered to provide legal support over my decision and drug dosage. They were in the last phase of making Metacam available as a licensed drug for cats. Their clinical trials had all had much happier outcomes than that suffered by

Smudge. The drug representative assured me that Smudge must have had a pre-existing kidney condition.

Eight months after I received the initial letter from the complaint committee, I received a letter outlining their judgement. They completely exonerated both Shari and me. We were deemed to have chosen a clinically sound and ethical course of action.

I was relieved, but not so convinced about the ruling. I was reminded of the chiropractic slogan "Drugs kill, pushed or prescribed." I started to distance myself from the medication component of my practice. I wanted the chiropractic adjustment to stand on its own. If more pain or inflammation control was required, I advised the patient to seek a prescription from their regular veterinarian.

Kev and I were not quiet about our distrust of the side effects of drugs. When Savannah had her tonsils out, she was the first patient to be discharged because she had steadfastly refused any pain medication. Kev and I realized we had brainwashed our children into an inflexible anti-meds mind set. We had to tell them that sometimes, pain control is beneficial and healthier than stoicism. Kev and I both occasionally take Tylenol or Advil. Our kids remain reluctant.

Borrowed Horses

IT STARTED WITH A SMALL innocent offer.

"Would you like to take some horses home over the summer?" Dena asked. She was our previous horseback-riding instructor. I adjusted her horses regularly and had seen the herd grow beyond the number of stalls as Dena succumbed to the lure of different horses for sale on the Internet.

I was so tempted. I had been craving horses of my own since my first riding lesson at age seven. When I attended a two-week riding camp at age twelve, I had fallen head over heels in love with "Sugarfoot", a small chestnut gelding named for his white sock. Sugarfoot had attitude, and was not popular among the teens at camp. He was assigned to me for the session. I was responsible for feeding him and mucking out his stall before my own breakfast, and then riding him three hours daily.

Sugarfoot was notorious for charging home during trail rides, and for bucking after every jump, and kicking at anyone who approached, without warning. I soon caught on to his ways, and gave him ample warning when I'd approach. I learned to anticipate, and sit through the bucks, and slow him with a half-halt the moment he surged toward the barn.

He loved to jump, and we started winning every mini-contest staged at the camp. I spent the free hour of quiet time we had between chores and lessons curled up in the straw of his stall, reading fantasy fiction or British riding adventure books.

When I heard that horses could be leased for the winter, I started a campaign to persuade my parents.

"It won't cost you a thing!" I assured them. "My babysitting money should be able to cover the board," I naively promised.

My sister Jean volunteered to share with the costs and be equal partner in the riding.

My parents agreed and said they would pay half the board if Jean and I would pay the other half.

My grin was so broad that my cheeks started to twitch with the muscular activity.

When I heard that Sugarfoot wasn't available for lease, we were offered a quiet dark gelding called "Sergeant", instead. I remained exuberant. We trailered Sergeant to a stable in the south shore of Montreal, a half-hour drive from home. Grade 8 was taken over with car pooling and long drives to the stable five days a week. My Bank of Montreal account, proudly started at age seven and earning around ten percent interest, started to dwindle with monthly withdrawals of $200. By mid-April, both Jean and I had exhausted our finances. I cleaned stalls to help defray the cost of boarding Sergeant. He was returned to camp in June.

Sergeant was a kindly horse, but also a lazy, sluggish horse. I never bonded with him the way I had with Sugarfoot. I heard through the stable grapevine that Sugarfoot came up for lease option the following summer. I had no money so I was pretty heartbroken. That horse was definitely my first high-school crush.

Dena's offer, some twenty years later, was perfectly timed. We had no barn or fencing, but we had a hundred and sixty acres of space. Kev started looking into fencing options as well as sourcing a barn. We found a local farmer who built cedar-post fencing strong enough to house an elephant. The sister of one of my equine clients offered to sell us their cow barn if we were game to move it thirty kilometres to our property.

I looked at the enormous cow/calf barn aghast. Each beam had to be marked and dismantled, then moved and reassembled at our property.

"This is crazy," I protested. "I don't need a huge barn, you know. I just need a small lean-to."

"The horses are for you," Kevin explained. "The barn is for me."

"Hank" and "Cloud" arrived in a trailer that summer. I would gaze out my kitchen window in delight. Horses made the most beautiful and entertaining of lawn ornaments.

Cloud was a placid paint gelding, wide in the beam and happy to cart an endless stream of children on his broad back. He was a drawing card for the kids' friends and cousins.

Hank was a chestnut teen with lots of energy and attitude. I was the only one equipped to ride him, and I took him for long lopes in the back field and along our ski trails.

I begged Dena for the option to buy Hank when they were returned in the fall. She was equally smitten by him, sadly. My enthusiasm for him may have increased his value for her, or triggered a bit of jealous pos-sessiveness. I was not given the option to take him home the subsequent summer.

A client heard I was willing to stable and train horses, and offered to bring his new mare, "Sapphire", to our home the following summer.

She was a shiny, dark-bay thoroughbred mare, shy, and unschooled. I had no faith in her not rearing or bucking me off on a ride, so the schooling was restricted to our small one-acre paddock. Sapphire was easily spooked and couldn't be trusted to be alone with the kids in the barn. They were unable to ride, and I returned her to her owner in the fall with little regret.

I was leery about offering a home to a difficult project again. A horse who was a risk to children and no pleasure to ride was not the smartest act of charity when hay had to be bought, water supplied daily, and stable chores performed without compensation.

Then I met "Kye".

Kye was a slope-backed, chronically sore, Connemara gelding whom I adjusted every two months at a stable three hours from home, way too far to increase my adjustment scheduling. His owner, Hillary, begged me to take him home as a project.

"I'll pay for the weekly adjustments," she assured me. "I'll save anyways by not paying the travel costs for you coming here. He's a valuable horse if his back would just get stronger. And I'm happy to spend the money."

Kye arrived for the summer. Kye was a finicky guy. He tolerated me riding him but would balk at anyone else on his back. I adjusted him weekly, initially, and then every second week as he got stronger. His topline changed and he became noticeably less swaybacked and no longer quivered in pain with pressure on his withers. He started to approach rather than retreat when I would heft his saddle onto the fence in preparation for a ride.

At the end of the summer, Hillary arrived with her trailer to pick him up. He had a straight topline, was well-trained and had excellent pedigree. She was optimistic about selling him at great profit. I bid him a sad adieu and retreated to the porch as she manoeuvred the big truck and trailer down the driveway. Suddenly, I noticed big eyes at the back of the trailer. I should only have been seeing a tail!

I charged down the gravel driveway in my bare feet, yelling "STOP!" at the top of my lungs.

Luckily a car was approaching on the main road and Hillary was forced to stop to yield. She heard my yells.

We opened the rear gate of the trailer. It was a side by side trailer, designed to transport two horses, with a metal bar partition between the animals.

Kye had managed to snap the rope securing his halter to the front of the vehicle and had wedged his head under the partition. He was folded in half in an awkward yoga pose, with the bar compressing his back. He was pretzeled. Kye was making a high-pitched keening sound of pain, one I had never heard before from a horse, and would hopefully never hear again.

I charged to the house grabbing Kevin's toolbox. We hammered upwards at the wedged bent pin keeping the bar in place, until it shattered and released. Hillary backed Kye off the trailer. He was shivering, sweaty and white eyed. It was obvious he was not going home that day.

We decided that I would keep Kye an additional month and adjust him again to resolve the new spinal issues resulting from the accident. I was unable to touch his back for a full week. The bar left a hairless welt mid-back. Even a light touch caused him to flinch. Two weeks later, I was able to work on Kye's back with his trust and confidence. I adjusted him almost daily for the first week as the muscle spasms would fight any holding adjustment. By the end of the month, he was back. I could saddle him, ride him, and groom him with no evidence of the injury.

Hillary called at the end of August. "I'm sorry, Alison," she announced. "I can't afford to pay for any of the work you've done for Kye. I'm going to give him to you. I don't think he would climb on my trailer ever again anyways."

No protest on my part had any effect. I offered to waive any fees, but she was adamant about not picking him up and not wanting him home.

I was in a conundrum. We had a paddock, an unheated cavernous barn, and a water trough we filled by hose. There were no winter options for housing a horse. I put the word out locally that I had a horse for sale.

I had worked with horses for over thirty years at this point, but Kye surprised me with a new trick. Every time a car drove up and someone emerged and pulled a saddle out of the car, Kye would start to limp. It was a dramatic head-bobbing limp. He was inconsistent on which leg he would favour, however.

The occupants of the car would shake their head sadly, and express concern about purchasing a lame horse. Once they had driven away, Kye would cavort happily, running the line of the fence with abandon. He clearly did not want to be sold.

Eventually, a woman who ran a small riding school decided she would take Kye home for her son. Given his limping antics, I agreed to let her take him home on spec. If he continued to limp, she would not be obliged to buy him. I set a price based on my summer costs only. It seemed a fair price for a purebred, well-trained Connemara.

I learned a new facet of human behaviour through the transaction that year. Kev has always maintained that people can be counted on to act in their own self-interest. I was much more of a Pollyanna. In this case, Kevin was right. In the spring, I got a phone call from the woman who had taken Kye, demanding payment for boarding him over the winter. She had decided to get a different horse for her son and no longer wanted Kye. She was demanding a monthly boarding rate which was high by city standards, unheard of in the Valley. I balked.

I spoke to my lawyer who assured me I was in no way obliged to pay. Then a friend from another local stable called to let me know that every-one was being told that I was bilking this woman and couldn't be trusted. The Valley is small. I paid the full amount with as much graciousness as I could muster.

Rather than trailer Kye back to our home again for more disruption, I offered him free of charge to a young client on the understanding that we would split any profit he generated if he were sold. I heard nothing further and was just relieved that he was comfortably homed and no longer costing me anything.

I ran into Kye three years later. He still recognized me and sported a white stripe mid way across his back to mark the trailering accident. I learned he had stayed briefly with my young client and had been sold three times since, each time at increased profit. It would underscore my complete ineptitude as a horse dealer.

A Horse in the Family

IF KYE HAD BEEN OUR last boarder, I would have been happy to give up on owning a horse. A summer with "Cindy" and "Stormy" rekindled my interest.

Cindy was a chesterfield of a horse, a Belgian Hackney crossed mare in her late twenties. The mix produced a gentle giant. She was joined by Stormy, a thirty-year-old Shetland pony whom we boarded as a favour to a friend. Cindy was a joy to ride, always good tempered and unflappable. Her hackney gait paired with the warm-blooded Belgian breed, made her the smoothest of rides. There was almost no reason to post when she trotted, and her canter was as relaxed as a rocking chair. Savannah became an adept rider on her back. The boys were less competent but were convinced of their prowess because she was a tolerant babysitter with novices on her back.

Stormy was merely a cute lawn ornament and occasional crowd pleaser for pony rides when my younger nieces and nephews visited. She primarily provided companionship to Cindy. One morning, I looked out my window to see Stormy lying quietly in the deep grass. I put away breakfast and emptied the dishwasher. Still no movement. When I went out to check, I was shocked to find she was cold and not breathing. She had passed calmly in her sleep. It was a sad introduction to death for the kids.

Stormy's owner was relieved that the demise was on our watch, and that her children were spared witnessing the death. I was happy there had been no evidence of stress or pain. It was still an awful experience. Cindy luckily seemed completely sanguine about the loss of her companion. She grazed unconcerned as the knackers arrived to pick up Stormy's corpse.

Cindy was sadly returned to her riding school in the fall, and was boarded by a student the following summer. If she had been younger, I would have gladly bought her. Late twenties made a second Stormy experience far too likely.

I had been craving a horse for thirty years. Cindy and Hank had whetted my appetite, and it was increasingly hard to say goodbye to horses we had gotten fond of when autumn came. Kev watched my emotional roller coaster and started lobbying for us to buy a horse.

A client in Arnprior called announcing, "I have the horse for you, Ali!" She took pride in matchmaking for horses and owners. She was temporarily boarding a six-year-old gelding from Montreal who was trained as a hunter/jumper. I was invited to go for a test ride on "Jack".

Jack was a stocky quarter horse, a dark bay with big feet, a good feature in a breed prone to laminitis, a vascular disease plaguing small-footed horses. He seemed to be a friendly fellow, and I set off on an optimistic trek.

Jack was energetic and responsive. When I gave him his head on the return to the barn, Jack let out an eager buck and took off full throttle. I reined him in, but still returned minutes ahead of the other riders.

I had been getting frustrated by the placid older horses I had been boarding, and the grumpy school horses I had been riding in classes. This feisty gelding was an exciting change. I agreed to take him home for a month trial.

Jack settled in rapidly.

Our Irish wolfhound, "Fen", took great delight in chasing Jack around the corral initially, but then Jack would lower his head and charge at Fen. It was clear they were both enjoying the game. I explored the trails, which branched from our land and crisscrossed the government-planted forest, with Jack, Fen trailing us at a comfortable distance. My animal world was complete. I signed the cheque happily at the end of the month. I had a horse of my own!

The kids were less enthusiastic. Jack was a challenge to ride and had a bad habit of throwing a buck when asked to canter. I learned to ask for the gait change when riding him up a hill, keeping the buck manageable. I did not feel comfortable letting the kids ride him except at a gentle pace in the front corral. They were responsible for keeping the poop cleared from the field. So their fun was limited and work was maximized. Their antipathy for the dirty, smelly chore was matched in equal measure by the pleasure my in-laws derived from seeing their grandchildren labouring in dirty jeans with pitchforks and wheelbarrow. I was happy to instigate the clean-ups when Kevin's parents came for supper. It spared us any judgement about raising soft, spoiled, modern children.

I was thrilled with the new family member. I rode almost daily. I trained Jack to approach when I whistled, with regular bribes of apples and mints. I kept his saddle and halter handy on our deck. I could squeeze a ride in when I could find an extra forty-five minutes of free time. Jack and I explored the trails that Kev was regularly carving out on our property, as well as strayed into the adjacent land of government forest. Muscles I hadn't used since high school got strong again, and I no longer winced with inner thigh pain after riding.

Kev argued that when Jack and I went for long fast rides, only Jack was benefiting from the fitness. I argued that riding was strenuous exercise.

One day, I wore my Garmin watch, which measures heart rate.

I looked down smugly as the watch recorded my heart rate as I cantered: 155, 156, 157 … It climbed into a respectable aerobic range.

Then when I noticed that it jumped from 159 to 200 then 201 … I realized I was reading the time of day! When I switched functions, it registered a heart rate of 64, sadly reinforcing Kevin's bias that only Jack was truly working.

Having a horse in the summer was terrific. The kids enjoyed Jack even though most of their interaction was in offering him treats and pats and the dreaded poop shovelling.

The fall offered the best riding with a respite from horseflies and mosquitoes and exquisite rides through the colourful trails.

When school resumed, the kids discovered that Jack loved the chance to share the last of their cinnamon buns or cereal when they headed off, and he would greet them eagerly at the end of the field when the school bus dropped them off in the afternoon.

November marked the limit of easy horse ownership. We were not equipped with the water source or hay needs for overwintering a horse. I boarded him at a local riding arena and arranged for lessons with the owner, Martha.

Jack was much less fun to ride in an arena. He grumbled about going round and round in circles and had to be urged on to complete a loop at a canter.

His attitude would change the moment Martha set up a jump. His ears would perk forward and he would willingly jump any height she set. If it was too small, he would always buck in protest.

Fen and Jack greeted each other eagerly when we trailered Jack back for the summer. By Jack's third summer with us, Savannah had developed enough riding skills for me to let her ride alone in the paddock.

When she asked if she and her best friend, Kiki, could take him out on the trails, I agreed. They saddled Jack up and Sav rode him while Kiki tagged behind on Savannah's mountain bike. They agreed to take turns. It was reminiscent of my pseudo horse bike when I was their age.

They returned two hours later. They were a bit giggly and reticent to share any details of the ride.

Savannah confessed that night that Jack had bucked them both off and had to be caught after a long chase in the back field. I was relieved neither had been injured, but didn't allow any further expeditions. I concluded that only I had the skill-set to sit through his bucking.

It was during Jack's fourth summer with us that Fen died. Jack became more cantankerous, was reluctant to be saddled, and would kick out when his feet were picked. He became uniquely my job to handle, groom, and feed. In retrospect, he had just lost his companion. Horses are intensely social animals, relying heavily on their tribe to alert them about dangers. Fen's death had deprived Jack of his herd.

One morning, I headed out to feed Jack and couldn't find him anywhere. I hunted in the gully behind the trees, looked in the barn shadows, and the shelter behind the barn. No Jack! I followed the fence line and found one of the fence boards was broken and tilted down at an angle. I clambered over. Sure enough, there were horse prints leading through the woods.

I notified the police, neighbours, and Kevin at work. I was terrified he would cause a crash or injure himself on the roads.

I threw on some running tights and shoes and headed out for a run on the trails, calling Jack's name every few minutes. I had trained him early in our relationship to come immediately when I called, initially with ample sugar-cube bribes. But there was no response to my calls.

I emerged on the road, many kilometres from home, and started running back toward the house. My neighbour, Alice, drove by and stopped. She was out looking for me. She said Jack had been found twelve kilometres away. We stopped at the house for me to pack up his saddle and bridle.

She drove me to the farm. Jack had found a herd of sorts. He was being held in a field with five llamas, all staring at him balefully from a far corner of the field. Jack was shaky and seemed delighted to see me.

I saddled him up and rode him home. He was sweaty and tired from his escapade, so I couldn't push the pace. I, too, was tired and covered in cold sweat after my run. It was a very long, cold ride home.

I tried to provide some stimulation for Jack and took different routes on our trail rides. One day, I elected to explore a fallow field in my neighbour's land, a huge uncharted bushy area bordered by forest and swamp. When I rounded a corner, I let Jack have his head. The trail was used by four-wheelers and I could see there were no potholes or gopher holes to risk Jack's legs. What I did not appreciate was that we were on a compass trajectory for home. Jack was headed for the barn!

As we approached a cusp of trees, I started to gather up the reins to slow Jack's wild gallop. He lowered his head and bucked. I didn't know a horse could buck at such a speed. I flew over his head.

I landed on my hip and stared furiously at the retreating back of my horse who didn't once look backwards. I got to my feet awkwardly and started lurching after Jack. Luckily, he did head home, not on another wayward adventure.

When I managed to limp back the five kilometres of trail, I found my neighbour, Alice, had again come to the rescue and had tied Jack up to a fence post. I wrestled the saddle from his back, removed the destroyed bridle, which had been broken in his mad dash through the woods, and closed the fence. When my adrenaline finally plummeted, I found I couldn't even climb the stairs to my house.

I was hobbled on crutches for several weeks. My hip was a black mottled bruise and I required regular adjustments from Kevin to get my pelvis back into working order. I sadly withdrew from a Half Ironman I had signed up for, and was a reluctant, cheering, supportive wife for Kevin as he ran the race. I continued to adjust horses, but my driver and assistant, Cindy, had to move the bench around for me and support me as I climbed up awkwardly on my stool to position myself for the adjustments.

It was over a month before I could finally walk with no limp. Kevin volunteered to ride his bike beside me when I took Jack out for his first ride since my fall. It was early autumn and duck hunting was in season. I was walking Jack at a sedate pace when a shot ran out. I don't blame Jack for reacting. He launched into a rodeo buck. I slid off gracefully and landed on my feet and was able to restrain him by the reins. Both Kev and

I were floored by the slow-motion buck. Jack had almost exceeded the vertical. There was no defying gravity and staying on. My ego, which had suffered from my first fall, was restored. But my confidence in riding Jack was completely gone.

Jack needed a new herd. And I was loathe to lose any more races due to injury. I realized I was more vested in my triathlon training and racing than I was in riding. I started looking for a new home for Jack.

One of my clients had started a riding school. She was always full of smug confidence that no horse could unseat her. And she was not a little woman. I had noticed that Jack was much more effective at launching a buck if his rider weighed less than a hundred and forty-five pounds. It seemed like a good fit.

I agreed to part with Jack for one third his original price. Horse dealing is clearly not part of my skill-set. I continue to adjust him for free every time I visit the farm. He always greets me with affection, but seems happy to be housed with ten or more equine friends. And he continues to buck off any light rider.

TriRudy Award

I MET THE JANES WHEN they brought their ancient lab, "Barney", to see me after he had torn the cruciate ligament of his left knee and could barely stand.

"No way are we doing surgery," announced the taller and bolder Jane. "We paid for surgery for Juniper when she tore her cruciate, and she was miserable and sore for months."

"And we had to pay for a second surgery for the other knee, less than eight months later," interjected the second Jane, a spunky redhead.

"Yup! I was just getting to that," Jane One finished,

The Janes were a lovely educated couple, youthful, fit, vegan, and loudly lesbian, living in a rural corner of Ontario populated with Mennonites, farmers, and conservatives. I got to know them well in the three years they survived the area before moving to a much-more-kindred British Columbia.

Barney was a big clownish lab. Generally, I advocate surgery for torn cruciate in large dogs. The body lays down scar tissue that acts to stabilize the knee when the cruciate ligament is no longer preventing the lower limb from sliding forward below the knee. In small dogs, the body's inflammatory system eventually creates some natural stability, but bigger dogs keep breaking down the bridges just due to supporting their greater weight.

The Janes were adamant about choosing conservative measures over surgical intervention. We embarked on an adjustment program every two weeks so Barney would not develop compensations as he manoeuvred on three legs. By the two-month mark, he was looking competent on all four, and he never injured the second knee, which the Janes marked as a huge success. I ended up seeing Barney and the Janes regularly until they moved out west. We became good friends.

We chatted quickly during office visits, trying to cram in as much social exchange as possible without setting me behind schedule with a full waiting room of scheduled patients.

"Why aren't you doing the TriRudy award?" Jane One asked as I finished up with Barney's back, always ending with a quick palpating of both of his knees.

"The what?" I asked as they headed out the office door.

"Google it," Jane responded.

I did that night. I discovered a website linking a community of like-minded triathletes and cross-country skiers based in the Ottawa area. Rudy Hollywood was an aging athlete who had been crazy enough to race in five local races in one calendar year. The races were iconic Canadiana. The first was a Winterlude triathlon including a skate on Ottawa's Rideau Canal, which boasts one of the longest groomed skating paths in the world. This is followed by a ski along trails in an urban park, and culminates in running along the treacherously slippery ice of the canal.

The second event is either skiing fifty-one kilometres classic, or skate-ski in the Keskinada Loppet in the Gatineau Hills near Ottawa—or completing the Canadian ski marathon, a two-day 167-kilometre event of classic skiing in Quebec.

The final three are warmer climes activities. The first is the completion of a two-day, 320-kilometre bike trip from Ottawa to Kingston and back. The last two can be completed anywhere: a full certified marathon, and finally an Iron distance triathlon.

It sounded daunting, but was mad enough to inspire ten or more individuals annually to submit their races to, and qualify for, the TriRudy Award.

Needless to say, I was intrigued and challenged.

I had never raced the Winterlude triathlon. My skating history was a month or so of lessons on arena ice on wobbly ankles and achy feet when I was seven. Graceful swan-like teens whirled by with sequined tutus as I careened into the wooden arena boards to bring myself to a halt. I eventually learned the rudiments of the craft enough to enjoy skating on the canal with my siblings in our adult years. Even as an adult, I preferred to skate in the company of my dad or my younger, but much bigger, and hockey-skilled, brother Andrew. They could tighten my skates without sending my fingers into freezer blocks, and hold me by my mittened hands to stabilize me and swing me along.

I took some crude lessons with a teenaged daughter of a colleague, and paid her to teach Savannah, too. I could skate without falling and without too many awkward moments, but only if I kept both blades firmly on the ice at all times.

Kev and I bought some attachable blades for our skate-skiing boots, and I started to actually like the sport. No more cold feet and frozen hands as the laces were tightened. No more wobbly, sore ankles, and frozen cramped feet. These speed blades were also the mark of a prepared Winterlude triathlon competitor. It meant you could skate into transition, whisk the blades off, and slide into the ski bindings in a minute or less.

In preparation for my first winter triathlon, I started skating once a week for the month leading up to the event. I skated with my great friend, Kirsten. She could skate circles around me, but accompanied me to keep me company and less conspicuous at the 11 AM to noon open skating hour. It catered to seniors. They were admitted at a discount and dominated the hour. Kirsten and I would chat our way around the rink as septuagenarian and octogenarian men and women whizzed past us impatiently.

I persuaded my sister Jean to join us in the race. Kirsten, Jean, and I wisely started at the back of the crowd. Racers at the front started in a crouched position, ready to launch into the low-backed, arm-swinging tempo of seasoned speed skaters.

At the one-kilometre marker, we were widely spread out. I trailed the pack with my stable two-blades-on-the-ice technique. Kirsten was far ahead, mid-pack. The front of the group was an organized peloton of skilled skaters moving as an airfoil with arms in sync, low body posture, and matching rhythm. They were a joy to watch as they swished by me on the return from the half-way mark.

The eight-kilometre skate was followed by a ten-kilometre ski. I made up ground on this section, skiing past less-seasoned skiers awkwardly herring-boning their way up hills. I was able to shout encouragement to Jean and Kirsten as we passed each other on the out-and-back sections of the course.

The last leg was a run on the canal. I had been pre-warned about the treachery of running on ice. I attached metal grips to my runners. They were awkward, slippery, and noisy accessories on pavement, but invaluable for running on ice without having one's feet fly out from underneath.

Cheering spectators lined the finish line on Dow's Lake, and everyone was treated to hot chocolate and cookies. We celebrated our finish with a hot tub at Jean's house. It was a very Canadian and thoroughly fun event.

Part two of the TriRudy Award was also new to me. I have often participated in the Canadian ski marathon, but had never raced the local Keskinada skate-ski race.

I arrived to skate-skiing late. The family learned as a unit when Logan was four years old. The three kids were soon skating circles around Kev and me, but we eventually caught up. Skate-skiing is exhausting when it's done poorly, but feels like flying once it's mastered, or even semi-mastered. I signed up for the fifty-one kilometre event, even though it was thirty kilometres farther than I had ever skate-skied. I survived. No finesse, and definitely no speed records, but I finished ahead of the cut-off time and earned my second medal of the year.

Rideau Lakes Tour is an annual out-and-back bike tour along the very scenic watery corridor between Ottawa and Kingston. Cycling with one thousand-plus Lycra-clad, like-minded bikers makes the distance feel shorter. Cars give wide berth to the cyclists. Most accidents are caused by drivers being oblivious to the presence of cyclists on road shoulders. During the tour, cars would have to queue to pass groups of ten or more cyclists, all wearing a kaleidoscope of neon colours, and often two abreast. The drivers were generally cordial, but even when irked, were unlikely to hit a cyclist by accident. I revelled in the seeming safety net.

That year was the first of many years of participating in the cycle tour. Kevin, Keith, and around five other friends joined me in the event. Kevin and Keith took more than their fair share of time at the front of the pack allowing those of us who were slower bikers to keep up as we relaxed in their slipstream. I earned my third component of the TriRudy medal in this epic event.

The Ironman medal I would earn that year came from the Esprit Race in Montreal. This is a Sisyphean-style event in which you go around and around and get nowhere, but do so with the constant presence of cheering friends and family. It is set at the Olympic basin in Montreal. The venue is used for rowing races, and is one of the only Ironman distance races in which you truly get to swim a mere 3.8 km, since you can actually follow a line on the floor of the basin and swim in a straight line. The race is held in September when days are getting shorter and nights colder. As a result, the swim is often frigid. Kev and I were both thoroughly blue when we emerged into transition.

The bike is forty-two loops of the Formula One racetrack. Although an odometer is very useful to keep you apprised of your progress, the announcer lets you know when you are entering your last few dizzy laps.

The year we elected to race was rainy, windy and around 6°C. I could hardly feel my toes, and my fingers had settled into the grey/blue colour of my Reynaud's-prone digits. I shivered my way into transition and headed into a washroom equipped with an electric hand dryer. Ten minutes of repeatedly pushing the dryer button allowed my hands to thaw enough to battle the unclip button on my bike helmet.

Kevin was so obviously hypothermic in transition that he was quizzed on the names and ages of our children before establishing enough mental acumen to be allowed to continue.

I ran by a friend who had come to cheer us on as I completed the first lap of the forty-two kilometre run. The run circles the rowing venue nine times. On the last lap you are rewarded with a broad hair scrunchy signalling that you are almost done. I glared jealously at runners sporting a scrunchy on their wrist as I completed the first few circuits.

"This is crazy!" Becky said, hugging me and trying to restrain me. "You are killing yourself. Please stop." She truly had tears in her eyes.

Who knows what motivates me and all the other crazy racers. I can't say it's fun when the fingers are frozen, the legs are like dead meat, and all you really want to do is curl up and sleep. But one soldiers on, passing and being passed by, limping, grimacing, occasionally vomiting competitors, and then break the finish tape, grinning ear-to-ear. After a day or week of heartfelt "never again!", one finds oneself Googling other Ironman race venues for the subsequent year. It really is a mad addiction.

Kev and I finished the run overheated after its frigid start. The husband and wife team who organize the non-Ironman-branded Iron distance race were there to personally congratulate every finisher. They host the competitors and their families to a breakfast the following day, and finishers get a warm sweatshirt to commemorate the event.

I ended up racing Esprit two more times in subsequent years. There are several different distance events run concurrently.

One year, Savannah, aged fifteen, decided to enter the Olympic distance race. She was initially trepidatious, but became adamant about racing when she was told she had to be sixteen to compete. Nothing motivates the members of my family more strongly than a NO!

It was very fun to pass Savannah—and be passed by Kevin—at different stages of the bike as we pedalled around the 4.5-kilometre track, repeatedly cheered on by Forest and Logan from the sidelines.

The final race for the TriRudy was the completion of a marathon. It should have been old-hat for me as I had raced over twelve marathons by then.

Squeezing in a marathon after a late season Ironman is a bit of a challenge to tired legs. I ran the Montreal Rock and Roll Marathon. The first half was fun. The second half was saved by the bands who lined the course every kilometre. My energy would flag, but then I would find myself dancing along with the lyrics of ABBA or the chords from *Chariots of Fire*. It was not a pretty finish, and most definitely not a Boston qualifier, but I had completed the fifth leg of the Award!

In November, I congregated with twelve other equally insane individuals to eat dinner, drink a well-deserved glass of wine, and to collect my TriRudy plaque from Rudy Hollywood himself. Other recipients were collecting their second, third, or even fourth award.

Hmm, I thought, apparently out loud.

Kev groaned. He knew me well. He knew I was plotting to return for a second one.

Trials of Fifty

TURNING FIFTY IN NO WAY dismayed me. It was the fun of entering a new, and hopefully weaker, age group in the Ironman. I enjoyed surprising people with my newly minted middle-age racing category. There's something about fifty that sounds so much older than forty-nine. I was typical of most Ironman triathletes. We all look much younger than the age stencilled on our calves at the start of the race. Of course, by the end of the race, we usually look a decade older than our biological years.

I had every hope that this year would have me finally posting a time and position to take me to Kona. The world championship Ironman race held in Kona, Hawaii, in October every year, is an absurd carrot that motivates every athlete, sometimes to ridiculous extremes like cheating or doping. Winning one's age category, or coming in among the top two or three competitors in large age groups, garners one the opportunity to do the crazy day-long affair all over again, after paying an outrageous entry fee, gouging hotel prices, and travel to Hawaii. It makes no sense. But I was as focused on this coveted carrot as many of my fellow competitors were. I had finished first in small Ironman distance races, and claimed 11:28 as my fastest time, albeit on a flat, non-Ironman course. I figured my cohorts must be getting slower and older in the fifty to fifty-five age group, and an 11:45 would place me on the podium in most races. I was gunning for this to be the year.

I recruited the help of Lisa Bentley, a coach and winner of eleven

Ironman races despite being diagnosed with cystic fibrosis. Lisa is one of the most optimistic and generous people I know. My brother-in-law Keith calls her the friend whom I pay. I was happy to do so. I asked her to help me with a six-month training plan to get me to the finish line with some bounce in my step. My Ironman run has always been a slow shuffle and a rather painful spectacle.

I was crazy busy at work, averaging a hundred and fifty animal clients a week. I had bought some time off, though, by hiring an associate, Sabrina, a chiropractor who had trained with me during her summers while in college. She was happy to take over my patients when I needed time off, and was to take on clients I could not accommodate. The kids were older and independent, with Savannah in university and the boys in high school. My life was fairly streamlined and easy.

We elected to spend a week's vacation in the family cottage in the Laurentian Hills. Cornu Lake has been my one consistent home between family moves as a kid. My grandparents bought it on their first arrival from England in the 1950s. I know the lake like the surface of my hand, and the roads are quiet and familiar for biking and running. Kev and I geared up for a week of uber triathlon training.

On Saturday, June 12, we headed into the local village of St-Adolph-d'Howard for a bike/run workout. My right knee had been plaguing me since a hilly run three weeks earlier. Lisa had been giving me strict advice to avoid running for a few weeks. I had a fifty-kilometre hilly repeat bike workout scheduled. Kev geared up for a long run, two eight-kilometre loops around Lac St Joseph. We parked at the public launch and arranged to meet two hours later.

My bike was great fun. I chose a quiet, recently repaved road and flew up the hills. The return was fast and mainly downhill. I was cruising along at speeds of around 50 km per hour when I saw a phantom police car parked inconspicuously in a driveway. I glanced down at my odometer to ensure I wasn't speeding. I always thought there would be great boasting rights for getting a ticket for going over the limit on a bike, but truly had no real zest for a ticket or run-in with the Sûreté.

Around two kilometres later, the road descended sharply before tapering off then cresting a hill before a stop sign. It was a nice, safe spot to comfortably give gravity full rein. I was tucked down on my aerobars, minimizing drag, when I spotted a car suddenly slowing in the approaching lane. The car started to turn left, directly in front of me, into a driveway on my right. I straightened and feathered the brakes, knowing it was impossible to stop. The choices flashed quickly: straight would land me on the car hood, right would take me under the wheels. I braked and swung left. I could see a woman in the passenger seat with her mouth in the O shape of Munch's *The Scream*. The driver was looking down at his lap. We collided and I flew.

I opened my eyes to see a policeman looking worriedly down at me. I wiggled my toes. Movement! I was alive and not paralyzed! I was thrilled.

"*Allo. Ça va? Peux tu bouger? Comment tu nommes tu?*" I was being asked in rapid-fire French.

I replied in French that I was fine. Just needed help getting on my bike and I would continue on my way.

Several hands restrained me. The ambulance driver, who had also materialized in those first few seconds, urged me to stay quiet while they secured my neck in a spinal brace. I was lifted onto a stretcher and placed in an ambulance. It was several weeks before I twigged that I had been unconscious for a while during the time period when these emergency workers had all miraculously appeared.

I urgently asked the policeman to locate Kev. I gave a description of the car and rattled off the licence plate and the location where Kevin had parked. It turned out that both the name I furnished and the license plate were complete inventions of my addled brain. Luckily, the van was one of the few vehicles at the marina's parking lot.

Poor Kevin returned from his run, hot and dehydrated. He was happy he had beat me back as it gave him time to pick up some Gatorade from the store. When he emerged, he was greeted by the police holding my bike in two sadly warped parts.

The kids have recounted the next part of the story to me:

Kev drove to the island and greeted them with a terse "Pack up your stuff. Mom was hit by a car. We have to go to the hospital."

They packed with alacrity, none of them daring to ask Kev whether I was conscious or even alive.

They arrived at St-Jerôme hospital to be stymied when they asked to see me. No one by the name of Alison Seely had been admitted.

In a room of unknown dimensions and unknown inhabitants, I lay on a gurney with a chart labelled "Aislinn". My neck was encased in a cervical brace, so I couldn't move. After an orderly took my vitals, I was left lying there for several hours, with no pain medication, and no idea of what was happening. I was tearfully overjoyed when Kevin and the kids finally found me.

I was given Tylenol, radiographed from head to toe, and pronounced healthy enough for discharge, with a broken collar bone and two fractured ribs. When a nurse wrestled my bike jersey over my head, she asked what was injured when I screamed. I let her know my clavicle was broken.

They gave me a sling and advised me to not work for two weeks.

We drove back to Ottawa avoiding bumps in the road as much as possible. When we stopped for the mandatory ice cream in Lachute, Kev gaped at my shoulder when he buckled me back in. My clavicle bones were tenting the skin, with the broken ends splaying at an awkward angle.

We stayed at Keith's in Ottawa and he arranged for an orthopaedic surgeon friend to see me the following morning. The X-rays were repeated, and it was now concluded that I had a wildly displaced clavicle fracture that was likely to become an open fracture without surgery. And the two broken ribs were more-accurately assessed as five, with one being a flail rib, or broken in two places. It turns out that although I adjust one bone at a time, I break them in happy multiples.

Kev looked over the shoulder of the orthopaedist and commented that the AC (acromion-clavicle) joint looked unusually wide, possibly indicating a dropped shoulder. We were reassured that the X-ray could be misleading when the clavicle is fractured.

I was in surgery two days later and had a radiographically gorgeous repair with a titanium pin.

When Kev helped me dress the following morning as we prepared for discharge from the Montfort Hospital, he swore. "Crap. You have a completely dropped shoulder."

Twenty minutes later, with yet again more exposure to electromagnetic radiation, a diagnosis of a fifth-degree shoulder drop was confirmed.

Sadly, a newly minted clavicle would not bear the torque stresses of a dropped shoulder repair. I was referred to a third hospital, the Queensway-Carleton, where Dr. Young was adept at repairing mangled shoulders using the patient's semitendinosus, a long tendon component of the hamstring muscles of the leg, to recreate the three torn ligaments. I was scheduled for just before Christmas so the clavicle would be comfortably knit before the stresses of the new repair.

Having an associate during all this was an enormous relief. My first text as I left the hospital in St-Jerôme was to Sabrina, letting her know her finances were going to be radically boosted, and her free time seriously reduced in the next few months. She rallied to the task gamely. With one arm confined to a sling, I booked the summer off work. I developed an awkward one-armed swim which kept me sane, and I biked slowly to Netflix films on a stationary bike. I also let Lisa Bentley know that my training should be put on extended—if not permanent—hold.

Kevin and I had several athletic adventures penned into the calendar for the summer. The Ironman in August was obviously going to be a no-go with my Nemo-like one-armed swim. We were also scheduled to fly to Scotland two weeks after the accident, and ten days after the clavicle repair. In early August, we had also committed to doing a seven-day haute-route bike race though the Pyrenees with our friend Steve. Scotland was non-negotiable for me. My entire family, siblings and children, were planning to visit our ancestral cottage in Northern Scotland.

When I was a child, we used to spend every second summer in Scourie where the smell of peat and the wet windy air felt more like home than almost any other trigger. I was determined to go.

The trip was fantastic, infinitely better than languishing on a sofa or bed.

We hiked every day with my arm firmly restricted in a sling, and our adventurous grownup kids would dash off-trail when it was clear I could not keep up. We ate meals as a family of seventeen, visited with second cousins, and played hours of card games.

We tackled a local mountain, Ben Stack. Kev and I chose to follow the meandering pedestrian track since I had no balance on the steeper hill.

Savannah, Forest, and Logan struck out directly for the summit, bushwhacking, rather than following a boring prescribed route. When we met back at the car at the agreed time three hours later, we were greeted by three scantily clothed offspring, all in their underwear. They were picking little black things off their skin and laughing a bit frantically.

Forest told us that they had flopped down on some heather near the top of the mountain when he saw he was covered in black dirt. When he brushed it off, he saw that it was moving. It turns out they were relaxing on a mound of ticks!

The clothes were covered in ticks, and we kept finding them hidden in body crevices. Kev and I were not immune. We continued to find them on our persons for the next three days, even as we ditched the affected clothes and scrubbed our bodies. My broken ribs were sorely tested when I collapsed in giggles when Forest was asked to remove a tick from his brother's very private body parts one night when Logan discovered the unwelcome passenger while in the bath.

On our return to Canada, we elected to prophylactically subject ourselves to three weeks of antibiotics. Northern Scotland had apparently become a hotbed for Lyme disease. On my return, I continued to bike lackadaisically in our basement as I rehabbed the broken clavicle. We had committed to our friend Steve for the bike race, and more importantly had paid for it in advance, a sure way to ensure this Scot followed through on a plan. Kevin had predicted a six-week recovery for the broken ribs. The Thursday before our Sunday departure marked the six weeks. I did a trial bike around the eighteen-kilometre block with Kevin, with heart palpitations at every car approach. We dismantled the bikes into travel boxes and set out for Paris that weekend.

I think Steve was amazed and a little dismayed at my inclusion. He had fantasies of performing well among the French cyclists with a strong drafting partner in Kevin. Instead, Kev was my staunch supporter at the back of the pack. We befriended the weak and the untrained at the rear of the peloton. I especially became a friend of Nigel, the Lanterne Rouge, whose role was to take up the rear and finish just ahead of the daily cut-off time. If Nigel finished ahead of you, you were officially disqualified from the haute-route tour.

I was one of thirty-two women on the route, outnumbered by men by a ratio of 18 : 1. My shoulder prevented me from brushing my hair, driving, or generally doing anything that involved lifting it beyond the horizontal.

Miraculously, I discovered I could bike, particularly uphill, with little compromise. Descending was a different story. I am not a courageous descender at the best of times, and the switch backs of the French Alps are intimidating to a relative flatlander. With no real control in my left shoulder, I tottered at every left turn and could only manage it with a death grip on the brakes. I could climb the hills at 10–12 km per hour, passing people with every bend. The same cyclists would whiz by me on the descents, averaging 60 km per hour as I tremulously fought gravity to inch down the hills at 15–20 km per hour.

We averaged between seven and ten hours in the saddle every day, with two or three infamous cols daily. I recognized many of the vistas and names from Tour de France videos: Hautacam, Col d'Aubisque, Col du Soulor, Superbagnères …

We ate four enormous meals daily and tumbled into dead sleep nightly. My sleeps were interrupted by nightmares of descending the mountains. I think my fists clenched as frequently during the night as they did during the day. It was truly a white-knuckled week.

The only day that gave us respite from the 120-kilometre-minimum fare, was day five when we did individual time trials in Saint-Larry Soulan. This was a twelve-kilometre climb, with individual starts on a ramp. The ramp terrified me, and I geared up to play the dropped shoulder excuse as I lined up, hoping for a start on the ground level. Two places in front of me in line was Christian, an older cyclist who sported two prosthetics to replace a missing lower leg and arm. He had suffered a motorcycle accident years earlier, and competed in the haute route annually. He was held up by the attendants and then descended the ramp like a pro. I swallowed my excuses and climbed the ramp. I survived, and then enjoyed one of the only days where the going was all mercifully uphill, no down whatsoever! I acquitted myself nicely, one of the faster women on that day.

Our last day was meant to be celebratory. We had survived six days of the tour, and managed to stay ahead of Nigel despite all expectations to the contrary. Kev could easily have held a comfortable spot in the front third of the peloton. He would climb at his regular pace, as that is a hard speed to modify. He would then wait and freeze at the top of the mountain until I ascended. We would then descend together, Kevin ahead, pausing to wait for my slower descent. I would sometimes just continue past him, as my frozen fingers could not squeeze the brakes tightly enough to actually effect a halt on the steep hills. Kevin was a champion supportive spouse as he cheated himself of the fun of actually racing, and was hypothermic in his forced waits in sweaty clothes.

Day seven involved only one ascent, Col de Monté. After descending its far side, there was a flat 140-kilometre ride into the Haute Route's conclusion in Toulouse. There was a time cut-off for the ascent, which we achieved with an hour to spare. We then descended, with my dictating the turtle pace as bikers flew by on our left. When we reached the foot of the mountain, we were greeted by the support vehicle. A French woman, in tour clothing and with authority, told us we were disqualified and must relinquish our numbers immediately. We argued that the next cut-off was the 3 PM finish in Toulouse, and that we had submitted the col by the requisite cut-off. The lady told us, with the charm Parisians are famous for, that we would never make the next cut-off, and if we continued, we would be doing so on our own resources and cognizance. There would be no aid stations, directions, or vehicle support.

We biked with speed and fury. Kev set a blistering 35-40 km per hour pace, with me valiantly tucked into his slip stream. We got lost twice and added around ten kilometres to the trip. We finished with more than forty minutes to spare and were rewarded with having our numbers returned to us. Apologies were not offered.

We recouped in Toulouse, enjoying a day as tourists wandering through the city by foot. Every couple of hours, we would stop to ingest as many calories as we could. Generally, it was an epic week. I was relieved when the bike descent nightmares stopped.

Two weeks after our return, Kev did the Muskoka Ironman Triathlon, alone. I walked along the bike course, cheering him on. Logan joined me on the run course and we volunteered at a water station for two hours, enjoying watching the suffer-fest from a different perspective than as a participant.

I returned to small animal practice for two months, wincing any time I had to adjust a wiggly dog. I still couldn't raise my arm above midline.

In December, I was again on the operating table. Dr. Young harvested a foot of my semitendinosus from an incision below my left knee and rebuilt the missing ligaments of my left shoulder. My patient clients were again in the care of my associate Sabrina as I rehabbed in the dreaded sling again.

And in March, a third surgeon clipped off a recalcitrant fragment of meniscus from the left knee, a result of being forcibly evicted from foot clips in the bike accident. In June, I was finally back to work, adjusting dogs and horses, a full year from the accident.

A distracted driver's moment to check a phone or GPS had cost me a year of practice. I had also sat reluctantly on the sidelines during the Muskoka Ironman, as well as missed a cross-country ski season, bike races, and all the events that keep me sane. On a positive side, I had seen more of Logan's high school basketball games than work would normally allow. But I was hungry for my own athletic return. I was determined that one stupid driver would not dictate the end of my work or athletic career.

Dogs in the Family

THE ONE STAUNCH COMPANION WHO gave shape to the days I was confined to a sling and unable to drive, was my dog, Haka. He was there to walk with me, swim with me while I bobbed asymmetrically along with a one-armed stroke, and defiantly guard me from any imagined threat.

For years, we had no dogs at home. My allergies forbade having a house pet. The dog of my childhood was a stretch to label as a dog. Holly was the result of generations of selective breeding to remove any semblance of ancestral dog. She was a miniature poodle, weighing in at around eight pounds, and too small to launch herself onto a sofa without assistance. My mother had sourced her from a breeder, with great intentions, thinking a hypoallergenic dog would satisfy the family's craving for a pet.

Sadly, Holly was a lap dog, with strong allegiance to my mother's lap, and with very little tolerance for children. She particularly loathed Dugald, my youngest brother. He would alternate between trying to make friends, and then taunting her, piqued by his lack of success. Holly was especially crabby when she experienced her biannual pseudo pregnancies. She would cart a squeaky, fuzzy, stuffed chick around the house, produce milk from her teats, and growl at anyone who ventured near her nest, which was unfortunately in a central area in our busy kitchen.

It turned out that hypoallergenic was an optimistic claim. I lived with a low-level wheeze through out my teens, and my mom would bag Holly hair for me to inhale when we went on family vacations so that I wouldn't experience a full-blown attack on my return home.

Holly lived to a ripe old age with my parents who loyally tolerated years of incontinence and dementia. She adored my mother, and was cherished in return. I'm sure she would have preferred to have met my mom after she was empty-nested.

Each of my siblings went on to get large dogs as pets when they established their family homes. Kev and I held out because of the allergy fear. I maintained that my job allowed me to hug dogs daily without the burden of caring for one.

Then I met "Topaz". One of my clients, Leslie, bred Irish Wolf-hounds, gorgeous, enormous dogs, the polar opposite of the miniature poodle. Topaz was a breeding female, five years old, 145 pounds, and wheat coloured.

We were mutually smitten. Leslie marvelled that Topaz was more affectionate with me during her monthly adjustment sessions than she was with herself or with her husband and son. And I drooled over Topaz, hugging her without having to lean down, and burying my face in her ruff after adjusting her neck. I did so unwisely, usually paying the price with a wheeze, or swollen eyelids or lips, from an allergy assault. With Topaz: nothing! I had found my hypoallergenic dog wrapped in almost human hair and in a human-sized envelope.

When Topaz was retired from the breeding program, Leslie asked if I would be willing to provide a home for her. I didn't even hesitate to get Kevin's joint blessing. For twenty years, the one dog breed that would elicit a guaranteed positive response from Kev was a Wolfhound. I knew that he and the kids would be thrilled.

Topaz flourished at the farm. She had never encountered a lake or the freedom of running off leash. She cavorted like a wild horse, charging around our beach after swimming, and dashing after rabbits and deer scents in the woods. She stayed attached to me by an invisible leash on runs, never venturing out of sight. In the house, she insisted on accompanying me everywhere, even squeezing into the powder room leaving me very little room or privacy to use the bathroom.

When Topaz nosed a porcupine and sported ten deeply embedded quills as a consequence, she let me pull them out with no restraint or sedation. She tolerated being squeezed into a colourful T-shirt during hunting season, having the kids straddle her like a horse, and my demonstrating sham adjustments during animal chiropractic lectures.

Topaz was purebred Wolfhound with the genetic handicaps that accompany the breed. After a short year of being an integral member of the family, I noticed a pronounced lump on Topaz's femur. She started to limp. I brought her to my clinic and X-rayed the leg. My eyes welled with tears the moment I mounted the radiograph on the back-lit viewbox. There was a distinct pattern of starburst rays radiating from the thickened bone. It was pathognomonic of bone cancer.

We provided palliative care for Topaz for two months, trying to come to grips with the diagnosis. She was doped with painkillers and patched with fentanyl patches long before they had street value. I adjusted her almost daily to help with the compensating subluxations as she limped on three legs. We said goodbye when it was clear she was ready.

Losing Topaz left us with no appetite for another dog and the potential of another loss.

I was not sufficiently strong enough in my convictions when Leslie called me eight months later.

"I have a new litter on the ground," she announced. "Nine beautiful pups. They're Topaz's nieces and nephews. I immediately thought of you. Half price for all the help you gave Topaz."

The family council was a formality. We were all excited. We drove the kids out to see the squirming less-than-one-pound bundles of fur. We all fell for the smallest of the litter, a little grey brindled ball of uncoordinated energy.

Kevin proposed Fang as a name, an ironic offering for the most gentle of breeds. We opted for a variant, Fen, in keeping with the ecosystem theme of our kids' names.

"Fen" doubled, trebled, and quadrupled in weight daily. We brought her to puppy classes. The first class had fellow puppy owners oohing over her cuteness. By the twelfth week mark, she was segregated in a pen until the last ten minutes of the class since her size so intimidated both puppies and owners. This runt grew to be the tallest of her siblings and eventually weighed in at a lean hundred and fifty-five pounds.

She was always playful, with zero aggression hidden in her genome. Her size and enthusiasm were sometimes scary. When Forest broke his radius as an eight-year-old, Fen would delight in grabbing him ever so gently by the broken bandaged arm to drag him around. She once charged into Logan and threw him several feet into the air. And when Logan greeted me at the end of the driveway by catapulting into my arms, Fen took that as permission to do the same, letting me experience some air time as I fell over backwards, and was promptly licked from brow to chin.

Fen also encountered the long-quilled menace of the woods. Porcupines walk with a slow, pronounced swagger, a come-hither invitation to any predator. I was running in our woods, two kilometres from any road, when Fen charged off into the bushes. She yelped and came to my call, muzzle, tongue, and paws full of quills. I was able to remove the ones in her feet so she could walk.

I attached her leash and we took off at a run, heading for home. Adrenalin pushed Fen into a frantic pace, and I was pulled along in her wake. The trail was windy and full of ditches and hillocks. I put a leg into the base of a ditch and Fen tugged me forward, causing my leg to bend upward at the knee. I saw my foot come up to meet me as I fell, knowing full well the anatomy of what was likely tearing: cruciate and lateral ligaments. I got awkwardly to my feet and managed to gimp my way home. I entered the house and promptly burst into self-pitying sobs.

Savannah rushed to get Kevin. Forest took one look at Fen and ran out of the house to hide in our woods. We later learned that somehow

Topaz's quill encounter and her eventual demise to bone cancer were irrevocably linked in Forest's young mind. Seeing Fen full of quills and his usually stoic mom in tears convinced him that Fen, too, was dying. He ran into the woods to escape this harsh conclusion.

There had been too many brushes with cancer in recent years. Following Topaz's diagnosis, both my father and my sister-in-law Andrea were diagnosed with terminal cancers. The fear of the C-word was well-warranted in our household.

We had to round up Savannah and Logan, and hunt down a tearful Forest and bundle everyone into the car to get Fen to my clinic to anaesthetize to pull the quills.

My knee was a slower fix and I gave up running and walked with a limp for two months and had to swim with a pull buoy.

Despite Forest's fears, Fen did not succumb to bone cancer then. She enjoyed seven years as a key member of our family. Leslie let me know as each of Fen's siblings succumbed to the genetic Achilles Heel of osteosarcoma. Every time Fen emerged from our lake, a bony shadow of her hairy self, I would inspect her nervously for evidence of bony lumps. In her seventh year, I saw the tell-tale bump on her humerus, paired with the beginnings of a limp.

We didn't drag out the process this time. I didn't want Fen to suffer. I took her to my clinic and radiographed the leg to confirm. I was scheduled to work that afternoon, but the staff kindly cancelled all my patients as I sat tearfully with Fen, holding her head in my lap as a veterinary friend delivered the lethal injection.

Kevin and the family were resolute about no further dogs, no further heartbreaks. In the subsequent years, Kev and I remained adamant. The kids started mounting a noisy lobbying campaign for a pup which we studiously ignored.

One day, I led a mini-seminar for a 4-H club of eight- to ten-year-old girls at a stable in east Ottawa. I demonstrated the parts of the horse's anatomy and how I could move spinal segments easily. I could sense that

I was losing their attention. The girls seemed to be giggling and riveted on one of the girls sitting quietly in the back on a hay bale.

I walked over to check on the source of the distraction. A tiny puppy sat curled in her lap. I admired the pup and used the opportunity to discuss the different numbers of spinal bones in humans, horses, and dogs.

After the talk was completed, I cradled the puppy. She was gorgeous.

"What on earth is her breed?" I asked. She was a mottled mix of brown, blond, and black hair, shaggy, and leggy.

I learned that she was one of ten pups, the results of an accidental coupling of a purebred Harlequin Great Dane and a similar accidental mixed mom who was half Golden Retriever and half Bernese Mountain Dog.

"They are all needing homes," the girl told me with imploring eyes. "Do you want to take one?"

When I protested that I couldn't possibly take one since our family travelled too often, Cindy piped up. "Like it would be any inconvenience for me to care for your dog any time you're away."

I brought up the topic at family dinner. The kids were, unsurprisingly, hugely enthusiastic. Savannah was a little disgruntled at our timing since she was due to graduate that year and head away to the Maritimes for university. Kevin was open to the idea, partly due to that imminent departure.

We made no commitments to the kids but discussed it that night in bed. Savannah's leaving suddenly made us conscious of the ticking clock of an empty nest. We worried that Logan would be that most lonely of creatures, an only child, in four years. He was the noisiest proponent for a pet. We decided we would once more bring a dog into our lives.

I had huge hopes that the hybrid vigour of the three breeds would protect this pup from the heartbreak of bone cancer and other genetic diseases.

We called the farmers and told them we would take one. We chose a gorgeous, ballistically energetic, black male pup. I picked him up at the end of a long horse-call day in the east end of Ottawa. He curled in my lap like a hot-water blanket all the way home.

The kids blame this two-hour imprinting period as the cause of the pup's subsequent allegiance. This pup would be my shadow and protector for years to come.

We called the pup Haka. He was born the day we had returned from a two-month mini-sabbatical in New Zealand. The rugby team, All Blacks, start each game with the loud, tongue-extruded, foot-stomping, Haka Dance of the Maori warriors, more intimidation than aggression. The black, exuberant, and tongue-lolling puppy seemed aptly named.

Haka grew exponentially. We don't seem to grow anything small at our house in Beachburg: sons over 6'4″, a daughter over 5'9″, tomatoes like small cantaloupes, and dogs over a hundred pounds. He was a wild mix of his three heritages. His coat was a glossy black, but tufts of golden fuzz appeared in the summer to announce his Retriever maternal component. The Retriever part was less obvious in his behaviours. He would retrieve sticks or balls for five or six tries, and then lose interest. His winter coat showed the influence of the Bernese, and he was happiest presiding at the top of the snow mound made by the snow plough, rarely choosing to come inside, even when the temperature plummeted below −10°C.

He could run like a sprinter with the endurance of a marathoner. I have yet to find his athletic limits. When we head out for a ski, Haka inevitably votes for the longer path by perching at the top of the longer trail whenever it forked, even after thirty kilometres of my skiing, likely more like forty of the more-random Haka trail. My boys, in contrast, could always be counted on to choose the shorter route. Unlike the boys, Haka would not scowl or grouse when his choice was overruled.

During Haka's second summer with us, Kev and I were enjoying a moonlit skinny dip swim at dusk. We had just rounded the buoy on the far side of our lake, five hundred metres from our shore, when Kev swam into a massive hairy body. He yelped, quite sure he was being tackled by a bear. It was Haka, breathing rapidly with the adrenaline of his first swim, a one-kilometre, ambitious first swim. Afterwards, Haka could be counted on to be my swimming partner, especially if he was worried about my swimming with an unknown friend, or if I were injured. I don't think swimming is a pleasure for Haka, it's more that he embraces it as a necessary component of his job of defending the family.

And defence was and is something Haka specializes in! Newcomers to the house are subjected to the greeting of a hackle-raised, growling, barking, hundred-and-forty-pound beast. We maintained that it was more bark than bite but were never confident enough to put it to the test. We had no luck shaping the aggressive behaviour into a more-acceptable greeting. We opted to lock him in his quiet room with a chew toy when people first arrived.

Departures were no problem. When guests left, Haka would lean his considerable weight against them and beg for patting and attention.

We loved the Dr. Jekyll side, and chose to hide the Mr. Hyde character as much as possible. I had the illusion that Haka would not hurt a fly and that his barking signalled fear, not aggression. He disabused me one summer run when he encountered a large adult gopher in the field. He charged toward me, delighted with himself as he shook the creature side to side, breaking its neck and spraying the area liberally with its emptying bladder.

On another run, he disappeared into a swampy area and battled with an enormous beaver looking like it weighed over eighty pounds. The two beasts circled each other like prize fighters, lunging with teeth rather than fists. Haka emerged with a huge gash on his side where the incisor teeth of the rodent had met under his skin. It required more than ten stitches and a drain. We suspect the beaver did not fare as well.

When I was injured by the bike crash, Haka would not leave my side. He swam gamely, inches from my side, trying heroically to match my very slow one-armed pace. He had to swim circles around me so he wouldn't sink with the slow speed. He was clearly frustrated by my lack of a functioning arm. He would lean against the side where my arm was imprisoned in the sling.

At times, he was clearly begging an adjustment. Haka is a walking ad for chiropractic. When his sacroiliac is out of alignment, Haka cannot lever his large, leggy body onto the porch. He stands at the bottom of the steps, looking forlorn. One adjustment and he will cavort like a mountain goat, leaping onto the porch two or three steps at a time.

When my arm was out of commission, Haka would look at me plaintively from the foot of the stairs. I would manage to deliver a crude, one-armed adjustment. He definitely pulled me back into the working world by making me trust my skill-set again.

At seven years of age, Haka is a healthy, puppy-like dog who looks like a black lab on steroids. He is a wonder of arbitrary genetics, a non-reproducible "great mountain retriever" who, we swear, will be our last dog.

We hope his genetics give him the longevity of a tortoise.

Lessons from Charlie

AFTER MY ARM WAS REHABBED, I returned to practice with enthusiasm. I missed the rhythm of the days that work brings, as well as the horse and dog contact hours. I even missed the people who accompanied my patients, much as I argue that my introverted self would flourish in a world populated by animals and vegetation, and plus Kevin, Savannah, Forest, and Logan. I guess I would include a smattering of eligible likeable youth to ensure the production of some grandchildren …

One character I missed was Charlie, an emaciated, pack-a-day septuagenarian who brought her beloved lapdog to be adjusted every month.

If "Pikoo" missed an adjustment, he would labour at jumping up on Charlie's lap, and start peeing on the floor, rather than climb the five stairs to the split-level landing to whine at the door.

Charlie would reluctantly submit to any locum I hired when I was off on vacation, or rehabilitating the recently broken clavicle and separated shoulder, but she did so grudgingly. She was a proper curmudgeon when she was not pleased. She had violent opinions on everyone and everything. Luckily, our opinions tended to jive. I would usually build in extra time to accommodate our discussions about Trump, misogyny, Canadian politics, and the risks of gluten.

Charlie had a colourful past which she divulged in snippets over our six-year friendship. She had embraced her teen years in the '50s with an enthusiasm that was more accepted in the '60s and '70s.

I was there to celebrate when a daughter she had relinquished at birth tracked her down to kindle a relationship. I saw her disappointment as the daughter's needs and bitterness eroded any promise of a new chapter in motherhood. Charlie followed the exploits of my three kids with enthusiasm and a strong memory for detail.

I referred her to Kevin for her back complaints. Sadly, he saw the Mr. Hyde to the Dr. Jekyll she presented at my office. He could never satisfactorily return a body tortured by decades of smoking and hard living to the twenty-year-old flexibility and pain-free living we all crave.

In contrast, Pikoo would not complain that it hurt more to jump up on the sofa at age fifteen than it did at age two. If he could physically jump, he would jump. Charlie and I were always united in our attempts to keep an aging Pikoo healthy and comfortable.

Charlie wore a colourful assortment of clothes, remarkably stylish at her age, on her twiggy frame. She was an effective Value Village treasure hunter. The clothes were generally chosen for texture. Charlie was passionate about cashmere. After I admired them once too often, Charlie started bringing bags of cashmere sweaters she would find, that screamed Ali to her. Two of my favourite closet items are the vibrant-green, oversized, v-neck sweater and the striped, thigh-long sweater she discovered.

When I returned to work after my lengthy accident rehab, Charlie greeted me with a hug. Neither of us had much meat on our shoulders, but Charlie seemed especially bony.

Charlie's sister brought Pikoo to me on the next few visits. She informed me that Charlie was battling a lung infection. Kev told me she was pretty sick.

I called from work one Wednesday. "Hey, Charlie. I keep threatening to visit. Is today a good day?"

She answered that it was ideal.

I showed up with fruit and dog biscuits. She welcomed me into one of the prettiest homes in the Valley, decorated in paintings in the same eclectic, colourful pallet as her clothes. Charlie was a brilliant artist. The house overlooked the river where she would snowshoe or ski every winter and it was awash in natural lighting from the panoramic glass windows.

I settled in for tea.

"I'm so glad you could make it out today," Charlie announced. "I'm guessing my sister spilled the beans. I hadn't wanted her to, but I'm glad she did. I would have so very sorry to have missed saying goodbye to you."

I'm sure my face registered my complete bewilderment.

Charlie laughed and said, "Tomorrow I say goodbye to all this. I've had a great run, Ali. Why would I want to tarnish that with oxygen tanks, chemo drugs, hospital confinement, and all that loss of dignity? Nope! I'm going to exit on my own time and terms. I know Pikoo is in good hands with you and my sister, and I have a lovely doctor who will come to the house to make sure it all goes easily and comfortably. No mess at all."

She described what was clearly a non-winnable battle against lung cancer. She left no room for a tearful reaction. When I asked if she had planned for a last special supper or breakfast, she dismissed the question impatiently. "Nothing tastes good anymore, Ali. I can hardly stand to eat. But. Let me show you the outfit I've chosen to go in …"

She led me to her bedroom where a velour multicoloured pantsuit hung in pressed splendour on a hanger on the closet door.

"What do you think? You and I tend to agree on my crazy clothes. Do you approve?"

She may have been asking about more than the clothes. But Charlie and I had had our discussions about our mutual atheism, and I completely respected her bravery and stoicism. I had seen my dad languish through the last weeks of life with a body stripped of health and reason due to cancer. I completely understood this carefully crafted decision. I was humbled by being able to share some of Charlie's last day with her.

I heard from Charlie's sister that the day passed exactly as scripted, with a close friend, her sister, and Pikoo at her side. Although the government had passed a law deeming medical suicide legal, it was not an easy thing to orchestrate. Charlie had to search outside the community to find a medical doctor willing to do the injection. Everything was done on the quiet to avoid a media circus, or visits from the religious right, or well-meaning, but disagreeing friends.

I still wear my cashmere sweaters and think of Charlie, even though my cavalier laundry methods mean they are too small to wear in public. And I continued to adjust Pikoo monthly through his geriatric years.

Psychic Advice and Referrals

I STOOD ABOVE BAILEY'S BACK, preparing to adjust his misaligned lumbar spine, when Cindy called out "Wait!"

She had just found a note pinned to the board with my name on it.

She read it out to me: "Dr. Seely. Bailey has told my animal communicator that he is very sore in his low back, and he wants you to spend extra attention to his left knee. He says thank you so much for making him feel better, and that he is less scared of jumping since you started working on him. I'll send the cheque on Tuesday. Hope to see you in person next time. Thanks from both Bailey and me. Joannie."

I continued to adjust, calling out the listings for Cindy to note down. And sure enough, when I climbed off the stool to check Bailey's extremities, I found the left intermediate carpal to be poorly moving. The carpus is technically the equivalent of the wrist bone, but horse people often label the joint the knee, because it flexes backwards much like a human knee. I added a note to my files for Joannie, acknowledging the "vision" of the communicator.

This was not my first encounter with a communicator. "Bruno", a show dog I adjusted monthly, apparently told her communicator he was miffed because I was missing the first rib on the left. When I checked the rib, Bruno almost bit me, but the rib was subluxated, and I had overlooked it.

I learned to identify the furtive look that inevitably preceded the admission that a new patient had been referred by their animal communicator. The source would vary. I had referrals from communicators in Ontario, Quebec, all over the States, and even in Australia. It turns out that geographic proximity was not a requirement for a reading.

The client would send a photo of the animal, and answer some questions by e-mail or phone, transfer a payment, and then get a detailed reading of the causes of their animal's angst. For some reason, the communicators were very passionate about chiropractic and were often very detailed about where and why the animal needed to be adjusted.

The readings sounded very specific, but other than the one who identified the first rib, were actually very easy to be accurate without any profound knowledge. A "sore back" or "headaches" was often identified. It would be a rare chiropractic session that wouldn't support those sorts of generalizations.

One owner was told her horse was being spooked by the baby. The woman was confounded until she recalled that a horse in an adjacent field had been called "Babe" when it had arrived as a yearling twelve years earlier. She took that as evidence that the communicator was doing a true reading. My interpretation was much more sceptical.

The most compelling story was relayed to me by Lena, the manager at a busy boarding stable in the east end of Ottawa.

The picture of a bay mare that I adjusted regularly was e-mailed to a communicator in Florida. I was told that the horse had told her, "I don't like the fat woman. The man is too hard on my mouth. But I do like the girl."

The fat woman could have described the woman who paid me to adjust her horse. She was a corpulent woman in her mid-fifties whom I had met only once. Lena was delegated to collect, un-blanket, and hold all the horses for me when I arrived. Lena was quite delighted to pass on the assessment from the communicator. I gathered she was not a big fan of the heavy owner. She said that the owner's husband sometimes rode and she wasn't at all surprised to have him described as heavy-handed. She was confident that the "girl" was the teen who co-leased the mare.

It was a compelling story of coincidences. I couldn't completely judge as it's hard to know how much information was volunteered at the reading.

The story was repeated regularly, so successfully convinced most of the owners at the barn to get their horses "read". Most of the reports confirmed that the horses were happy with their owners who gave easily fulfilled wishes like more grain, more regular grooming, different turn-out schedules, but sometimes expressed the need to be adjusted.

Obviously, my scepticism was not a wise face to wear in the face of this bounty. And the horses all did need to be adjusted. Of course, any animal who is forced to carry a saddle and rider while having a metal piece wedged in their mouth is going to have spinal issues, so it didn't take an accurate psychic reading to predict that need.

But I am an optimist, a very superstitious atheist, and I would love to find some magic in the world. My earlier encounters with psychic readings had all been disappointing.

My mother, whose level of credulousness is only matched by her claims to be a sceptic, had paid for a psychic reading for us both when I was in my early twenties. In fairness, we stumbled on the self-proclaimed clairvoyant on a street corner in Vancouver. She did not come with any testimonials or recommendations.

She gave my mother a revealing reading as my mother nodded her way through the descriptions of her diseased parents.

Then it was my turn. I turned milky, vacant eyes on her and adopted a slack-jawed, credulous smile. I blushed when she asked about romantic interests. She assured me that I would get over him, that he was unavailable, and that my efforts at work would be noticed, and that I would likely be promoted. A spot-on reading for a secretary who had unfortunately fallen for her married boss. Sadly, a little off kilter for a PhD candidate who was happily living with the man she loved and would marry seven years later.

My mother bore the disappointment well and deemed the money well-spent in scientific inquiry.

Thirty years later, I decided to squander my own dime in the pursuit of science. With so many stories from clients I liked and respected, I decided to submit my own questions to an animal communicator. I put Haka to the test.

My dog is one of the happiest dogs I know, embracing life with unbounded enthusiasm. But I know he has one festering beef. He is not allowed in the house due to my allergies. The rule has been flexible, though. If there is a thunderstorm, Haka adopts the saddest, most forlorn look as he quivers in fear. The kids would inevitably break down and sneak him into the house and bury him in covers beside the bed in the basement. We would also let him in when it seemed the safer option than leaving him outside to "greet" strange men, with teeth barred and hackles raised. He would enter with alacrity when invited inside. To leave was a more challenging matter and he would either have to be dragged out, no easy task with a hundred and forty pounds of solid rebellious muscle, or bribed out. It would take a growing mound of delectable treats with the kids or me nonchalantly relaxing on his bed in the sunroom, which was his domain, before Haka would venture to leave the fun of the inner house. When he was house-sat at Cindy's, he was allowed full rein of the house. He apparently laid claim to the sofa and would be returned to us happily fat and slothful when we got back from our vacations.

I knew any animal communicator would have to identify Haka's desire to be inside if they were to convince me they were truly chatting with him.

I was careful to be honest but non-forthcoming in my communication with the psychic. She offered assessments by phone, Skype, or e-mail. I opted for the last. I thought that left me the least risk of betraying information by voice or facial expression, the currency needed to drive a "cold reading". I figured I would minimize the risk of a "hot reading", where information is gleaned from the Internet, so I submitted the questions from Kevin's e-mail.

I sent a picture of Haka and identified him by name and age.

I asked, "Is Haka happy? What could I do to make him happier? And how do I discourage him from being aggressive to strange men?"

The answers arrived within four days.

It was generally advice that anyone could have gleaned by a quick Google of any animal behaviour advice website. The communicator announced that Haka was happy, especially when fed, and attacks his food with passion. (Untrue. He always sits and waits to be allowed to eat, and will do so for minutes.) I was told he needs clear boundaries (very established); needs to know I am boss (I am the undisputed alpha male in the house, Kevin equally so); should be put in a separate part of the house when strange men arrive (never been an option); and is reacting to testosterone (duh!). She also suggested that he be called something less aggressive, like "Hank", and that I could purchase some flower remedies from her site for $30.

As expected, there was clearly no exchange of information between Haka and the communicator. I'm not even sure I got $69 of a laugh. Generally, I would say this particular service does not do any harm, although it does cost a fair penny to offer some general platitudes about one's pet. There is a ready market for communicators who pose as ventriloquists for the mute animals that are so important to their families. People are often desperate for some indication about the status of an animal they love. We are all keen on finding a Dr. Doolittle to interpret the barks of our voiceless family members.

I have seen people buoyed up by the assertions that their animal is returning from the dead as their next pet, or being told a lost dog has actually been abducted, or other versions of confident nonsense. With hefty bills for these readings, the psychics can prey on the vulnerable. To borrow the words of John Oliver in his scathing exposé on human psychics, they are occasionally "… guilty of being attention-seeking parasites who feed off personal tragedy like a human-sized deer tick."

Haka continues to thrive with his tail wagging and tongue position betraying as much information about his attitude as any reading could generate. He still stays outside, and we ignore his forlorn looks at the fireside, unless there is a storm.

And we still call him Haka.

He told me he doesn't like the name Hank.

Divided Practice

MY REBUILT SHOULDER WAS A modern miracle and far prettier than the step-wise shoulder I had prior to its reconstruction. It was capable of swimming four kilometres, but was sadly inadequate for many tasks. I would drop heavy containers, struggle with opening doors with my left arm, and was challenged with a dull ache and numb fingers when driving long distances with the hands in the recommended 10 AM and 2 PM positions. Although I could adjust small animals with little modification, horses posed more of a muscular strain.

Cindy would witness my wincing every time I adjusted the neck of a horse, or any especially large-bodied or resistant animal. When I finally announced that I was going to transfer the Ottawa side of my practice to Sabrina, and restrict my practice to local stables and clinics, Cindy was unsurprised. Likewise, many of my clients expressed that they had been surprised by my return to work and were supportive of the move to a smaller practice. They knew and accepted Sabrina from her locum work during my injury. It was a very smooth transition.

I had some odd die-hard clients who were reluctant to switch. One staunch supporter, and long-time friend, was Margot. She gamely tried to bring her dogs to Sabrina for a couple of months, and then decided she was happy to do the three-hour return trip to the Valley once she tracked me down. I was delighted to renew my friendship with Margot and her husband, Bill.

I had often joked with Margot that if were I to write a book about animal chiro, her dogs would fill one hundred pages. Margot always had eight to ten dogs on the go, and loved them with a passion usually reserved for single children or pets. She knew more about animal behaviour and training than anyone I knew, and certainly way more than we veterinarians could glean from the scant lectures we had received in vet school. She had a gruff no-nonsense way about her which occasionally intimidated the staff and Sabrina, but it was a veneer over a huge heart. When I teased her or joked, there would be a brief pause before a booming belly laugh.

The first dog I adjusted for Margot was a bearded collie, "Milly", with a recurrent ear infection. Margot had been unstinting in her treatments for the ear, washes under anaesthetic, and had worked her way through an arsenal of antibiotics, both oral and topical. Milly had a crusty, smelly ear that she was constantly scratching. Margot was clear that she didn't really expect chiropractic to help, and it was likely a ridiculous waste of money, but had been told by a good friend it was worth a try. I adjusted Milly, finding the atlas completely jammed on the side of the infection. I told Margot that the findings were very promising. She raised a sceptical eyebrow, but booked a recheck for the following week, regardless. She was cheerier and more forthcoming on the second week, telling me that Milly was scratching way less, and seemed to have less discharge. Margot announced that there was no point in being unscientific about it, so she was ditching any antibiotics and seeing what chiropractic, alone, could do.

The ear was almost clear on the third week. Margot and Bill were impressed.

Around one month later, I was introduced to a second dog in Margot's menagerie. "Poncho" was an agility athlete, and no longer wanted to jump. Luckily, adjusting his sacroiliac joints and lower lumbar spine resolved the issue.

Some of the greatest sceptics become the strongest supporters in my practice. They are generally people with strong opinions and a penchant to express them.

Margot became my loudest advocate. She referred dogs to me, weekly. If a dog refused a jump, walked with a wiggle, a roach, or a head tilt, Margot would tell them to come see me.

I got used to recognizing the arms-folded-I-don't-know-why-I'm-here stance of the people she would refer to my office. The number of reluctant doubters who followed her advice to see me was testimony to the enormous esteem her clients held her in. When the dogs responded favourably to being adjusted, and their presenting issues resolved, most clients stayed on for proactive care and became equally stanch supporters. Many even started seeing a human chiropractor for their own back complaints.

One day, Bill arrived with yet another dog, this one a Beagle who was more Bill's than Margot's. The beagle, "Fred", had a marked stripe of hairless area stretching from his shoulder to his foot. The elbow was raw from chewing, but the rest of the skin looked healthy and pink, despite being completely free of hair.

"What do you think, Alison?" Bill asked. "We have seen our vet about this, but he's completely stumped. He took skin scrapings and found absolutely zilch. This has been going on for over two years. I can't show him like this, and the itching is driving both Margot and me crazy."

"Pretty weird," I agreed.

I checked out the little guy. There were a lot of subluxated vertebrae, typical of a dog with a rowdy bunch of siblings, but most notably, the fifth cervical vertebra on the left was completely restricted. I adjusted him.

"No promises, Bill. But it's pretty significant that Fred is out of alignment exactly at the vertebral segment where the associated nerve innervates the dermatome where he is hairless. Let's see if that changes anything. In the meantime, maybe throw a long tube sock over his elbow. Once an area is itchy, it's very hard to break the pattern of chewing, and he's going to court a good skin infection the way he's going at that."

The following week, Bill informed me that the sock could come off. Fred's leg no longer seemed itchy.

One month later, Bill brought Fred in, with a smug smile. "Check it out," he announced.

I looked closely at Fred's left foreleg. It was covered in a light peach fuzz.

By the eight-week mark, there was nothing to distinguish one foreleg from the other.

I was now capable of no wrong in Margot's and Bill's eyes. When one of their dogs showed an illness or injury, they would seek my advice first before visiting their regular vet.

When Margot's dog "Twister" developed a raw patchy wound on her carpus, they immediately brought her to me. She had marked subluxations at the fourth and fifth cervical vertebrae with the telltale symptom of a brachial nerve irritation with an itchy lick granuloma. Chiropractic resolved the irritation and the campus healed.

Another dog stopped endlessly chasing his tail after sacral and coccygeal adjustments.

Margot started to bring cases that would normally constitute emergencies in veterinary medicine. When one of her dogs stopped being able to eat and had to be syringe fed, Margot brought him in for assessment. His temperomandibular joint was unmoving on both sides. Apparently, he had inhaled something the previous week and had sneezed vociferously, somehow misaligning his jaw. It was a one-adjustment cure.

When I abandoned ship in the Ottawa area, Margot continued to bring her dogs for regular chiropractic appointment for any of their sundry ailments.

When her Schnauzer "Bertie" developed incontinence that defied treatment, Margot elected to drive an extra hour to seek my advice.

"I know your replacement is good, but I figure if there's something spinal that's making her pee, you'll find it," she announced when she tracked me down and brought Bertie in to see me in Pembroke.

I assured them that I had an entire practice happily seeing Sabrina and all delighted with the results. I cautioned Margot that many conditions can cause incontinence, including an untreated urinary tract infection, hormone imbalance, cancer …

"Well, if you can't help Bertie, then I'll take her into the regular vet. But I've wasted way too much money being told they can't help, when you can. So I'll try here first."

The next few days, I received a continuous stream of text messages updating me as to Bertie's status:

"Dry all the way home. That is a first this month!"

"Still dry after last night. Peed a regular stream on our walk today."

"Two nights dry!"

"Still dry on day 3. Tell me if I'm texting too much please."

"Dry for full week!"

Chiropractic did not cure everything for Margot's and Bill's dogs. They were still victim to cancer, muscle sprains, and the merciless ticking of the accelerated time clock for dogs. But Margot continued to attribute most of the cures to chiropractic help. She single-handedly reversed many medical naysayers and sceptics. She was a hard woman to disagree with.

Another Rudy

WITH A SMALLER PRACTICE AND fewer work hours, my energy level was hard to rein in. I had been unseated from my bike while training for my third TriRudy Award. Just as Kevin predicted, one award merely whetted my appetite for another round of the five epic races. I had completed my second award the year after I achieved the first plaque. In 2014, I was happily in pursuit of my third. I had competed in the Winterlude triathlon, this time hauling all my sibs into the fun, along with my staunch companion, Kirsten. I had skied the Keskinada 51-kilometre race, and had run the Ottawa marathon. Just one week before I was hit by the driver, I had finished the Rideau Lakes tour. All that remained was an Ironman. Kev and I were in the Laurentians training for the hills that awaited us at the inaugural full-distance Ironman in Muskoka.

I have what the kids and Kevin refer to as a completion bug. I hate leaving anything unfinished. It is often a fault. I will soldier through injuries to finish events, leaving me with chronic injury, when rest would have resolved it. I will put things away in weird and impossible-to-retrieve-from locales just to finish cleaning in the last sleepy minutes before bed. I will finish books when the first chapter announces that I will hate it until the last page. Not a useful trait.

The third TriRudy loitered as an unfinished item as I regained my arm strength and mastered my swim again. I set out quietly to accomplish it.

Kevin had allowed his rowing to take a back seat to our Ironman training. He was now celebrating a break in the intense biking, and running to focus on long-distance sculling events. I knew my Ironman would be an individual effort this year.

The biking was no longer daunting. Kev and I had travelled to Majorca with Keith and his new partner, Jen.

Jen was a kindred athlete, an Ironman finisher, and a strong, fearless cyclist. I finished the week's biking expedition with newfound confidence on hills. I could not careen down hills with Jen's confident abandon, but was no longer having nightmares about the switchbacks that Haute Route had left me plagued with.

The first TriRudy race was now my favourite winter event. Kirsten and my sister Jean joined me in the Winterlude triathlon. I was unable to persuade my brothers to make this a yearly tradition.

Kirsten was also my ski marathon companion. Kevin was focused on training for the indoor rowing world championship held later in the month. Kirsten was eager to attempt her first go at achieving the Bronze Coureur de Bois, skiing the full hundred and sixty-eight kilometres in two days.

We ran into the first stumbling block early on the Saturday morning. We had set both my phone and Kirsten's watch for an alarm at the unappetizing hour of 4 AM, and had asked for a back-up wake-up call from the hotel.

When I woke, surprisingly refreshed, I reached up to check my watch: 5:10 AM was the terrifying number on my screen. My phone was dead, Kirsten's watch was out of battery, and the hotel phone was slightly off kilter.

We had a panicked breakfast and were reassured by an official that we could start at Section 2 and still be eligible for the Coureur status.

We started Section 2 at 8:15 AM, around forty-five minutes later than we would normally have started that section. We hustled all day, narrowly meeting checkpoint cut-offs, eschewing waxing help and snack breaks.

The day was a struggle, with blistering winds and frigid, slow skiing conditions. At around the sixty-kilometre marker, I came across a surreal scene. Shrouded in the blizzard of white, were three people crouched over a prostate man. He was completely grey. They were quietly doing CPR.

I announced that I was a veterinarian and asked if I could help. They assured me they had it well in control and asked me to hold back spectators. A group of skiers had grown behind me, so I created a body barricade in front of the group, and urged skiers by.

It was not long before a snowmobile arrived with a stretcher. I continued my ski. I paused and leaned against a tree several kilometres later, shaky, nauseous, and tearful. It was obvious the man had been dead. He was handsome, relatively young, and athletic.

The following morning, there was none of the festivity and music that normally heralds the start. We held a minute of silence to acknowledge the death of a fellow competitor. Although the race always had busy ambulances and helicopters evacuating broken bones, concussions, and hypothermic victims, this was the first death in the marathon's history. I finished the day with relative ease, and no time constraint issues.

When I arrived home that night, my sister Jean called, distraught with the news that a friend and colleague had died during the race. It turns out I had met him several times at social occasions at Jean's house. He was a fit radiologist, around our age. I had not recognized the grey, recently deceased skier as that vital man from the party. It was a sobering reminder about the fragility of life.

The following week, I received an e-mail letting me know my hustling had been in vain. The marathon committee had deemed my late start did not warrant being exempt from skiing all ten sections. I understood, but was bummed.

The next weekend, I elected to ski an alternative race, the Gatineau 51 K Skate-Ski Loppet, to fulfil the requirement for the TriRudy award. I had not been skate-skiing that year. My funky rebuilt shoulder was not up to the task of the strenuous poling, and I had put all my practice efforts into traditional skiing. I knew the race would not be a fast nor pretty affair, but figured muscle memory would carry me through.

The first fifteen kilometres were fun. Then my arm started to throb and I flagged.

At the twenty-kilometre mark, a lovely family waved and cheered me on lustily, and pointed me toward the path as it veered left. I smiled at their encouragement and skied on the narrow path that climbed a steep hill through the woods.

When I emerged onto the wider expanse of the parkway, I noticed that every other skier was sporting a brown number pinned on their jackets, not the blue one I wore.

I asked a fellow skier if this was still the right direction for the 51-K event.

She shook her head sympathetically, and told me the cut-off was five kilometres earlier, and that this was the route for the 27-K race.

I had been tight for time before the detour. To be eligible to finish the race, there is a strict time cut-off at the thirty-kilometre mark. I skied against traffic as I retraced my steps. I had to snow plough between groups herring-boning up the steep hill, glaring at me as I ploughed dangerously through gaps between skiers. I saw one man climbing the hill, also wearing a blue bib, in the sea of brown bibs.

"This is the wrong way. *Mauvaise direction,*" I told him in both official languages.

"*Ich verstehe nicht,*" he answered.

I panicked. "*Links, schlecht. Reicht gut!*" I stammered, forgetting all but the most rudimentary German in my time-crunch panic.

He shook his head, bewildered, and continued up the slope.

I returned to the intersection where the family had waved me on. The sign marking the 51-K direction had been shielded by their bodies.

I skied like a maniac, sloppy technique, but with lots of energy, and narrowly made it past the 30-K post without being eliminated. I was at the back of the pack when I finally completed the 51-K—or 59-K by my odometer—but I finished.

Next in line was the Rideau Lakes tour. This one was uneventful. I sadly missed the broad backs of Kevin and Keith to draft behind, so my time was pedestrian. Jiffy, my staunch friend from vet school, joined me. We chatted our way through the kilometres, discussing vet cases, families, and triathlon training.

The Ironman I chose was Mont Tremblant. It was close, familiar, and set near the family cottage where I could isolate myself from the Ironman hype and just relax with my family.

I had been training with my friend and coach, Lisa Bentley, when I was derailed by the car crash. She very graciously offered to train me through the two months leading up to the event.

She and I both knew that I particularly needed guidance in the taper phase. I tend to resent the time off training that a race demands, and train exhaustively until the day of the event. I had big hopes that the guidance would let me finally actually race the marathon portion of the triathlon. But genes, training, or just lack of stamina resulted in a good swim, pretty good bike, and miserably slow, gut-cramping run. All I needed was a finish, and I gratefully accepted my medal.

Lisa was irrepressible as usual in her encouragement and congratulations. I have never seen this incredible lady without a huge smile on her face.

The final event of the year was the marathon. I elected to pair the race with a visit to the Maritimes. Kevin and I are firmly of the unbiased opinion that Acadia is the best university in Canada.

Savannah ended up agreeing after our tour of the Atlantic provinces.

Forest started at Bishop's University in Lennoxville, Quebec, but transferred to Acadia after two years so he could continue to play basketball and study Physics.

Kev and I decided to spend Thanksgiving with him in Wolfville. We could showcase the school to Logan, hoping for a hat trick of kids choosing the school.

And I could run the Harvest Marathon.

The race is a beautiful and very quiet run up a series of hills over-looking the Bay of Fundy. I was excited to run in the locale where I had first been introduced to running by Kevin, thirty years previously. My first run at age twenty had me dying after four kilometres, learning pain-fully, that aerobic dancing does not make one an aerobic athlete. It was nice to return in my early fifties knowing I was stronger and fitter than my university self.

There is a cardinal rule of racing: Don't try anything new on race day. I have broken that rule umpteen times, and never to good effect.

When I geared up for the race in Nova Scotia, I worried about the effects of the hills, particularly all the descents, so I elected to try some prophylactic anti-inflammatory meds, definitely a non-chiropractic approach. I have raced with so many people who gamely pop some ibuprofen at aid stations and swear by the results. I thought I'd try to pre-empt the pain that generally accompanies the second half of a marathon.

The first half went splendidly. I took some ibuprofen at the 10-K aid station and washed it down with Gatorade.

At the turn-around, I was comfortably running 12 km per hour and feeling like it was an easy pace to maintain. Then my legs were seized by a vice-like cramp.

I stopped and stretched. I regained my speed.

One kilometre later, both calves contracted fully. I could not lower my heel to the ground. Spectators looked at me oddly as I contorted by a tree, trying vainly to ease the cramp.

I continued at a shuffle walk. My arms started to cramp. My hands arched into a wide, finger-splayed spasm when I tried to pick up a cup of Gatorade at an aid station.

I managed to keep moving forward, looking much like Quasimodo at times, and finished around one hour later than the family was expecting me.

I did some Googling that night at the inn. It turns out muscle cramps is a fairly common sequela to non-steroidal anti-inflammatory meds. One more solid reason to spurn medication. It reiterated the line that Kevin joked about posting on the sign at the office: "Drugs kill. Pushed or prescribed!" I should have been wiser.

Luckily, the TriRudy requires merely completing the events, no need for speed or finesse. I picked up my third TriRudy Award that October, happy to complete the process that a distracted driver had derailed. Luckily, too, I have always been ridiculously superstitious about numbers, so a third TriRudy encompassing my fifteenth marathon and tenth Ironman was a good one to end on.

More Breaks

ONE HOUR LOST, OR 468,000 seconds, is not much: roughly 0.0002% of my life. I have squandered many more hours with computer games, bad movies, and poorly written books. But losing an unretrievable hour of memory leaves a gaping hole which feels considerably longer. On May 28, 2018, I lost that hour.

I distinctly remember the first hours of the day. Kev and I had elected to bike for a couple hours on a Tuesday morning before Kev headed to Pembroke for an afternoon of patients. The morning was bright and clear, and we were training for yet another Half Ironman. We were on the last stretch of the bike, on our quiet block, five kilometres from home. I remember descending the hill on Zion Line … then nothing.

The next picture in my chronology of the day was being asked how I was doing, by Patrick, one of my equine clients. I was lying on my back on a gurney, Kevin by my side. I couldn't quite figure out why Patrick was there, nor why my shoulder hurt like the dickens. And why was I flat on my back? Patrick was a radiology technologist in Renfrew. My addled brain could not compute why he was suddenly in the room with me, and not in our normal meeting spot at his stable.

I asked Kevin why my shoulder hurt. He explained that I had been in a crash and had likely broken my clavicle. He was very patient. He later told me that this was around the tenth time I had asked that question.

I was groggily aware that I was being wheeled into the radiology wing and had a series of X-rays taken, and was then strapped into an ambulance and transported to the Ottawa Civic Hospital, sirens blazing.

The next two days passed in a blur of brief wakefulness with visits from Kevin, Forest, and Logan and a succession of exams by nurses and medical doctors.

When I slept, I was beleaguered by visions of the gaping maw of a ferocious looking bear. I'd wake in a sweat to escape the glare of the bear less than one foot away, and entwined with the front wheel of my bike.

I woke on one occasion to find Kev staring at me concernedly. "You are clenching and unclenching your fist repeatedly. What's going on?"

I told him I kept dreaming that I had to brake to avoid hitting a bear. I also reported seeing a bear cub which I was braking to avoid. But it was the big menacing head of an adult bear that kept interrupting my sleep.

Kev had not seen the cause of my accident. He had been biking strongly, around twenty metres ahead of me, when he heard me yell out. He swivelled his head to see me catapulting off my bike, head first into the pavement. He braked and turned the bike around. When he reached me, I was unconscious, head askew at an awkward angle, and drooling. He had a panicked moment of thinking I might be dead.

When I complained about tinnitus, or ringing in the ears, several weeks later, Kev laughed and said it might be a reaction to how loudly he had yelled for help. We were on a quiet country road. The nearest properties were several hundred metres away. His yell was sufficiently loud to attract help from both of the nearest houses. Within twenty minutes of the crash, an ambulance, fire truck, and police car were all on-site.

I think Kevin has fared the worse in each of my accidents. I know that witnessing Logan fracturing both radius and ulna in one ill-fated basketball game, where he hit the back wall too hard, was far worse for me than any of my accidents. It is easier to be the unconscious spouse than the one gazing down on a crumbled mess, wondering if she is alive or dead, brain injured or paralyzed.

Kevin had no idea what had transpired to make me fall. He assumed

I had hit a pothole.

I was useless as a source of information. I kept repeating in an apparently cheerful manner, that "My head hurts ... My shoulder hurts ... What day is it please?"

Kev explained repeatedly that I may have broken my clavicle again.

"Again?" I asked. "What do you mean, again?"

I was amazed as he informed me I had been in an accident three years earlier.

When I learned it was Tuesday, I kept reiterating that I should be heading to Carp to work. I had no memory of having severed that portion of the practice to Sabrina. I was amazed to learn that Forest was working on a summer project in Sudbury. I didn't know he was a student at Acadia.

When Kevin quizzed me further, he established that I thought Forest was still in high school, wiping out two years at Bishop's and one year at Acadia from my time line.

At some point in the ambulance ride to Ottawa, my eyes welled up with tears. I had just remembered that my dad was no longer alive. Dad had died nine years previously.

Memory came back slowly. I retrieved all but around one hour of it eventually.

The vision of the bear took more and more shape with each wakeful dream. I could see a baby cub dashing out of the bushes on the left and crossing the road in front of me. I braked and avoided the baby. Then I saw the big angry head of a mama bear right at the level of my front wheel. I always woke then, in a panic.

When Kevin returned to the site of the fall to retrieve my damaged bike, he shared my recurrent bear visions with the neighbours who were storing the bike. They were completely unsurprised.

"This is a bear highway," they explained.

Their property bordered a small forest directly across from a bushy grove in an otherwise barren sea of agricultural fields. They reported that a mother bear and her two cubs regularly crossed the road at that junction, sometimes being seen several times in one day. Later that summer, another neighbour confirmed the story. She told me the mama bear and cub were daily sightings. They had disappeared for a two-day hiatus after the crash, but were back unscathed the following week.

My recovery was considerably slower. It turns out hitting a bear is almost as unforgiving as hitting a car. I sustained fractures of the parietal and frontal bones of my skull, had a bleed on the opposite side of the brain from the ricochet effect, and fractured my right collarbone, and two ribs. Everything was on the opposite side of the body to my previous injuries this time.

My concussion symptoms were dramatic. In turns out that hitting the head repeatedly is not ideal for brain function. Headaches, dysphoria, and vertigo became my daily companions. I was also left with disconcerting erratic muscle spastic motions when I would stand up or gesture. Word-finding was problematic. These were all humbling experiences for someone who hardly ever experienced headaches, and is probably not the most sympathetic caregiver to those who do, and to someone who prides herself in being a wordsmith. I struggled to reclaim the equanimity I had found with the previous accident, where I celebrated being alive. This time I found myself wondering way too often "Why me? Again?"

I didn't remain in the wound-licking phase for long. The year 2018 boasted a gorgeous summer to enjoy during my house arrest. I was confined to home with no ability to drive and with an arm anchored in a sling, and hoping the clavicle would knit without surgery.

Haka was thrilled to have a daily companion. I hiked endlessly with him and perfected a one-armed swimming technique. My left arm had been left weaker and chronically sore after the first accident. It now became powerful as I swam upwards of three kilometres a day with my right arm tethered in a wet suit or just tucked inside my swimsuit top.

I filled the days with trying to polish my skills in German, and I also started working on this book. My mini iPad was ideally suited to my one-handed typing technique. I had briefly eschewed computers to cater to the concussion symptoms, but succumbed to the lure of *Words with Friends*, e-mails, and Duolingo for my German lessons. My intolerance of boredom and inactivity have likely always hindered any speedy rehabilitation.

I entrusted my practice to Amy, a local vet who was trained in animal chiropractic. I told her confidently that I would return to practice in July, then August, and finally, September, once my clavicle had healed.

Amy was very flexible with my waffling dates.

The bony ends of the broken clavicle were widely spaced and should have been tackled surgically. I had returned to Dr. Young, the orthopaedic surgeon who had rebuilt my left shoulder three years previously. The time passage had made a surgical correction less optimal and Dr. Young had elected to see if natural history would heal the fracture. It is said in the orthopaedic world that if you put two clavicle ends in the same room, they will find each other.

I had X-rays in July to test the hypothesis. There was zero union. We put off further X-rays—and disappointment—until September.

My injuries, and most especially, the source of the collision gave rise to a mix of incredulity and humour from friends and family. Savannah was working as a biology teacher at a high school in Guilin, China, and regaled her students and international friends with this example of a most-Canadian accident.

I Googled biker encounters with wildlife and was comforted to be in the company of other crazy victims of accidents, mercilessly recorded by their Go-Pros, as they were catapulted from their bikes from encounters with bears, deer, and even a kangaroo.

Once more, I was overwhelmed by the generosity of friends and family as they volunteered hours to help with the challenges of being one-armed and concussed.

Keith and Jen dropped by weekly, bringing supper; Kirsten came for lunches and swims, helping Haka in his life-guarding duties; my in-laws drove me to appointments, made supper, and did laundry. I was spoiled with week-long visits from Germany-based Sybil, Jiffy from southern Ontario, and my sister-in-law Cindy from Vermont. Accidents are a wonderful litmus for finding true friends.

When I was radiographed in September, I was optimistic. I had been swimming strongly and could even partially move the right arm without a clunk. I felt sure there was finally bony union.

The radiology technician knew of my veterinary training and allowed me to stand impatiently behind her as she processed the image then brought it up on the screen. I was interested in seeing what sort of ugly large callus had formed. I expected a big gargoyle of a mass bridging the bone ends: ugly but effective. But the image sharpened in front of me and my heart fell.

Minutes later, Daryl Young confirmed the bleak news that there was no callus whatsoever.

It turns out, if you tuck the bony ends in opposing corners of the room, it's a bit challenging for them to find each other. The distance between my clavicle ends was too big to bridge.

Sling Sentence Again

I CALLED THE EVER-ACCOMMODATING AMY and told her that she would be working as a locum for me for at least another three months. On the day I had scheduled for returning to work, I was instead suffering through the familiar pre-surgical fast, preparing to have a steel plate implanted over the right clavicle.

I was pretty bummed to be in a sling again. The energy and mood outlet that swimming provides was verboten. I was cautioned against doing anything that could possibly prevent the newly aligned bones from knitting. I was back to walking, writing, reading, and German lessons. I wore my Garmin watch and tracked my daily steps. Emptying the dishwasher dish-by-dish, and putting away clothes one item at a time, helped me reach my step goals of 12,000 per day, as well as provided some environmental enrichment to the long days. Forest and Logan had headed back to Acadia University. The nest was officially empty. It was not the best timing for a mama bird to lose use of a wing.

I returned to my favourite physio after the eight-week sentence of sling time had been served: the pool. My true favourite, the lake, was officially closed for the season under three feet of ice and three more feet of snow.

I started in the 92°F water at a local hotel where you can complete a lap with four strokes navigating around a geriatric social club. I soon progressed to the local Kinsman pool where my fellow swimmers graciously tolerated my presence in the fast lane, despite the slow, one-armed crawl. I slowly added more and more right arm contribution to the stroke. I had a hollow shoulder from muscle atrophy from six months in a sling, but was beginning to have the semblance of a normal stroke.

After sidling up to me in an adjustment-begging stance for months, Haka was delighted to get his first adjustment at the end of November. In December, I started seeing small animals at the Pembroke Animal Hospital again. Amy continued to cover my horse practice until I could regain a modicum of right arm strength. My patients were effusive about welcoming me back, as were their owners.

The 2018 winter was the snowiest one in years. I was delighted to be able to add cross-country skiing to my rehab. Kev groomed our trails and Haka and I powered through kilometres of skiing with my arm stronger with every thrust of the poles.

I signed up for the ski marathon in February. It was lovely to celebrate being back to working condition.

I called one of my long-term horse clients, Shirley, in mid-December. "I think I'm ready to take on horses again, Shirley. Would you like Button to be my first guinea pig?"

Shirley was one of my favourite clients. The first time I met her, I'd arrived at an empty yard and had no response when I knocked on the door. I had opened the screen door to call out hello, rousing an older, tail-wagging, overweight lab who was lounging by the woodstove.

A voice called out from the upper level. "Come on up. Come see what I'm up to."

I found a spry, older, white-haired lady kneeling in the far corner of a bedroom, finishing the final hammering of the new wood floor she was installing.

"There!" she announced with satisfaction. "I couldn't just leave it one plank short. And it's nice to have someone up here to admire it!"

I would always be interrupting some ambitious task that Shirley was tackling single-handedly when I arrived: haying, fixing fences, gardening, or baking up a storm for a charity event.

I also had to navigate the visits between her many passions, including belly dancing lessons and multiple absences for world travels. She embraced the activities on her travels like a twenty-year-old, and I would be regaled with stories of the excursions, and entertained by her photo albums when she returned.

I adopted her as a favourite aunt.

Shirley had first called me out to see her horse, "Button".

The mare was hobbled with laminitis and only chiropractic gave her enough relief to be able to move comfortably. It allowed Shirley to wean her off a heavy and pricey arsenal of drugs the vet had prescribed, and which were proving ineffective in controlling Button's pain.

Button deserved a pain-free retirement. She had a resume that boasted as much philanthropy as her owner's. She had regularly visited retirement homes where she would respectfully control her bowels and bladder while allowing the elderly residents to pat her muzzle and feed her carrots.

Shirley recounted one occasion when a gentleman in his nineties raised his head for the first time in months and stroked Button's nose, tears pouring from his eyes. He had been raised on a farm. Button's smell and feel had tugged him back into his childhood.

Button was a perfect first patient to test my arm strength. She was a miniature horse, smaller than Haka. I knew I wouldn't be overly taxing the recently healed clavicle.

I also always adjusted "Chaplin", Shirley's big black lab. He was lame and wobbly with an old cruciate repair on his right hind. I had recommended adjusting him when I first saw his awkward gait when Shirley had called me to see Button.

Both animals walked much more comfortably after that first visit. I started visiting every six to eight weeks. I would adjust Button, and then retreat to Shirley's warm kitchen to adjust Chaplin and exchange stories about Shirley's family and travels, and fill her in on the adventures of my three kids.

Button was small, but the technique for adjusting a miniature is identical to that of a bigger horse. My right shoulder withstood the torques comfortably. Shirley took pictures with my iPhone.

I told her I would post the pictures to celebrate my re-entry into equine practice. I had discovered that social media was the quickest way to communicate with my clientele: particularly as the word-of-mouth is a rapid transmitter of information in the horse world.

We picked up Forest from the airport the following day. Logan would be coming home the next week after a later exam. The boys had a two-week stint for the Christmas holidays before an early return for basketball season. The tree was decorated and the presents wrapped. I welcomed the anticipated bustle of the holidays after the quiet months I had spent at home without work, car, or children.

On Saturday, December 16, Forest elected to drive to Pembroke for a weight-lifting session. Kevin disappeared into the woodworking cabin for a mystery Christmas project. I decided to head out for a ski.

Haka danced around enthusiastically when I emerged in ski boots and gathered my poles and skis.

I walked to the top of the five stairs of our porch.

Whoosh!

My legs flew out below me.

There was an expanse of black ice under the skiff of surface snow and I crashed down the few stairs onto the cement pad at the base.

My arms were holding the skis. The pain at my right shoulder was blinding. I screamed so loudly in rage that poor guiltless Haka scuttled away in fear. "F————-k!!!!!"

Not again!

After belting out enough curses to forever scandalize my Mennonite neighbours, I got to my feet and went back inside the house. I was wearing a favourite shirt. I know the horrible fate for shirts in hospitals. I manoeuvred myself painfully out of the sleeves and pulled it over my head. With my nude torso, I approached the full-mirrored coat closet with trepidation.

Crap!

The big lump over my sternum looked suspiciously like a fresh break.

A full angry scream for around sixty seconds almost had me hoarse but didn't elicit any panicked, running feet from the cabin.

I pulled a jacket over my shoulders and some big boots with no zipper, and tentatively navigated down the icy stairs and approached the cabin door.

With trepidation, I knocked.

Kevin had been a stalwart supporter through what had now mounted to over a year of pain and neediness through both bike accidents. He had been the sole provider, chief cook, massage therapist, regular chiropractor, chauffeur, and family communicator.

When my arm was in a sling, my right hand would sometimes sneak out to spoon food into my mouth or write a note.

Kevin would freak. "No! Don't use your arm! You are going to slow the healing! I'm leaving if you screw this up, you know!"

He was joking. But was he?

He opened the door a crack. He blocked my view of his "secret project" with his body. "Yes?"

"Umm. I may have screwed up the surgery. I fell."

He thought I was joking. But then he saw that my wry face was holding back tears.

There was no yelling, no recriminations. Lots of self-directed ones though. A distracted driver was unavoidable. A bear was crazy, but again likely not my fault. But icy stairs? A Canadian cliché. I should definitely have been wiser.

We drove to the Pembroke Hospital to get X-rays. Kevin was hopeful that nothing was broken. When we paused at a red light, I pointed out the growing lump at my sternum.

Kev groaned. It was clearly either a new fracture or a sternoclavicular dislocation, or both. Neither was a good option.

I was triaged in emergency and rushed into care. They X-rayed the clavicle and took a CT scan.

The lump kept growing. By the time Forest joined us, I could no longer feel my right hand and my jaw was tingling. It was beyond the skill set of our local hospital.

Kevin had set the family triage system into action and had contacted my medical siblings. Andrew was on a skiing holiday at Mont Tremblant but was in phone contact with his colleagues in thoracic surgery at the Ottawa General Hospital. They agreed I should be transferred to their care.

The lump had everyone in a bit of panic. What was bleeding so ferociously? The thoracic inlet houses some vital vessels. The emergency team checked on the possibility of sending me by air. I lobbied hard for that choice. A helicopter ride would be a lovely bonus to this fiasco. Unfortunately, it looked like the time frame for arranging air transport would be longer than by ambulance, and time was critical. So I was once again enjoying the sirens and speed of an ambulance ride to Ottawa.

The emergency medical technician who rode with me assured Kevin he would be vigilantly monitoring me for the entire ride. Hardly reassuring words. His name was Will and we chatted all the way into Ottawa. The 150-kilometre route took fifty-two minutes. By the time we arrived, Will was vowing to send his girlfriend to see Kevin as a chiropractor, and was going to recommend his parents bring their aged dog to see me. I had entertained him with stories of chiropractic results.

As he helped transfer me to a hospital gurney, he confessed that he'd been convinced he would have to intubate me. He was relieved my lump had not worsened.

At the General, I was subjected to further X-rays and a second CT scan, and a night in hospital with an IV drip and nurse visits every two hours.

I was told the lump was the result of inflammation, not a life-threatening bleed. The recently repaired collarbone had fractured in three sites on the medial edge of the steel plate. I was given the choice to stay for up to a week under medical supervision, or go home. Easy choice. Forest arrived to pick me up midday.

I arrived home to the wonderful news that Savannah was so alarmed by my new fracture, she had elected to come home. She had three weeks remaining in her teaching contract in China, but was being granted leave to waive her last weeks of salary to come home and rescue her "frail grey-haired mother". That was the picture she painted to her boss, one that was readily accepted in a culture that venerates respect for the elderly.

The political climate between China and Canada had just recently turned from tepid to frigid with the Canadian arrest of Meng Wanzhou, the chief financial officer of the Chinese technology company, Huawei. Three Canadian citizens had been promptly arrested in China, without any apparent cause. The most recent was a young teacher.

We had no way of relaying our fears for Savannah's continuing to work there. The one channel of communication we had was WeChat, a medium that was scrutinized by the Chinese government. We may have been more anxious than the situation warranted, but it was a huge relief to know she'd be coming home. It was also brilliant to know all my kids would be home for Christmas. It was almost worth the new fracture.

Luckily, the summer months in a sling had honed my skills for cooking, eating, putting on clothes and generally functioning with just a left arm. My concussion symptoms, which had been abating, were back in full force with headaches, muscular spasmodic motions, and vertigo. I did enjoy the absence of rib fractures this time though.

I had to extricate myself from all my optimistic promises. I withdrew from the ski marathon, apologized to Sabrina as I reneged on my offer to provide a maternity locum for her, and engaged the ever-accommodating Amy to continue to cover for me in Pembroke.

The house was bursting at the seams with family and holiday excitement as we hosted Keith and Jen, and our nephews Quinn and Ben, as well as Savannah, Forest, and Logan.

Christmas morning unveiled Kevin's mystery gift. He had hand-crafted a gorgeous white cedar kayak paddle for me, one so light it felt hollow. He had researched it and had selected a Greenland-style paddle so it would be easy to manipulate with my mangled, weakened shoulders.

Four years earlier, he had surprised me by making a wooden kayak for my fiftieth birthday. It was the product of hundreds of hours of labour and secrecy in our woodshed.

My injured left arm had left me struggling with a typical stroke. This summer's left arm injury had compounded the challenges. The new paddle required little strength or finesse. I looked forward to the coming summer when I could test out both kayak and paddle, and rebuild some atrophied muscles.

The weeks in a sling whizzed by during the holidays. At the four-week mark, I was a little housebound with no driving, just endless stationary cycling and treadmill walking. I donned my ski boots and carefully navigated the stairs and tested my one-armed skills on our trails. I was obedient to Kevin's cautions on my first outing and only skied the hill-less loop he had groomed for me. Then I ignored caution and skied the entire hilly six-kilometre loop, feeling alive with motion and speed.

I was freed from the sling at eight weeks, and Kev and I travelled to the Azores with Keith and Jen to celebrate. I had added Portuguese Duolingo to my daily regime to prepare for the trip. I achieved enough fluency to merely be irksome, primarily adding a nasal *o* to Spanish words and concluding requests with abrigada.

I figure attempting to learn a fifth language is impressive in one's early twenties, and just eccentric in one's fifties. But it did while away some more hours during the sling phase.

My shoulder was frozen, an unsurprising sequela to the months it had been pinioned to my chest. The hotel boasted a warm pool and I once again took to the water to tease some movement out of the shoulder. We ignored the pouring rain and hiked daily, registering ten to fifteen kilometres on our Garmin watches. It was a great escape after two months of house arrest.

I once more called Amy and the Pembroke Animal Hospital to alert them of my proposed return to work in March. I had two weeks to unfreeze the shoulder. I was back in the Kinsman pool, again kindly allowed as an impostor in the fast lane as I navigated each lap with thirty-six strokes (my normal, and not very proficient rate, is eighteen, Kevin crosses in twelve), my right arm uselessly not contributing to any forward motion. I skied again with two arms. I added weights at the gym.

I was greeted enthusiastically by staff and clients on my return to work. I had also agreed to cover Sabrina at the mini-clinics held at Donna's kennel. It was marvellous to rekindle friendships with Donna and her husband as well as with clients I had known for twenty years. Equine clients would spot me at the grocery store, coffee shop, or gym in Pembroke and wrestle my promise to see their horses in April.

I called Shirley and offered Button a chance to be my first equine patient in four months. She accepted eagerly.

Most of my clients on the first day back were familiar, long-term regulars. Several had travelled from Ottawa to see me.

One new client was sandwiched into the schedule. Gwendolyn, a matronly woman carrying a very ataxic, friendly Basset Hound, was probably a little taken aback to see all the other clients greet me with hugs. She had been referred in by her veterinarian when a radiograph showed marked stenosis of the cervical vertebrae in her geriatric dog. The appointment was facilitated by not having to explain my series of two accidents in detail. We instead focused on the Basset, "Buster".

I adjusted his subluxated neck and recited a now-dusty spiel about risks of disc herniations and the advantages and disadvantages of surgery.

The following week, a beaming Gwen and a much-more-ambulatory Buster returned for the follow-up appointment. I felt like I had come home. It was so marvellous to be back fully and functionally in a useful role in a field I love.

Adventures Await

Two weeks after alerting Shirley that I was back in action, she telephoned with a tone of panic in her voice.

"Sorry to call you so late, Ali. Is there any way you can make it out to see Button tomorrow. I'm at the end of my rope. I'd call dead stock, but the ground is still frozen and I just don't see how we can bury her now. Maybe you can do something?" She faltered, clearly fighting tears. I assured her I would be out first thing in the morning.

I found Button lying in a bed of hay in the barn. Shirley had been wrestling some hay under Button's bum, valiantly trying to avoid pressure sores from lying in one position too long. The miniature horse had apparently been unable to get up for more than four days. Shirley was haggard from an almost round-the-clock vigil of hand feeding her and propping hay beneath her.

I palpated the spine and adjusted the misaligned segments. When I checked her hips, I found her dramatically askew. I assumed she had been three-legged lame with a recurrence of her laminitis. I couldn't adjust her sacroiliac joints in the prone position. I suspected the prognosis was pretty bleak if the laminitis was so painful that she refused to stand.

I felt down the small legs to check Button's stifle joints. I paused at her left patella, her knee cap. It was completely lateral, not snuggled in the groove where it should be sitting. With the leg relaxed and non-weight bearing, I was able to reposition the small bone back into the patellar groove. Shirley helped me manoeuvre Button back onto her four feet. I was then able to realign the left sacroiliac joint and restore symmetry and normal motion to the mini's hips.

Shirley was relieved when Button stayed on her feet and started to graze on the hay padding. She said she would let her neighbour know that he might not have to battle with the frozen ground any time soon. We both hoped that this recovery would not be a short-lived affair.

The phone rang again late that evening. I had just finished regaling the encounter to Kevin and I groaned when I saw Shirley's number appear on the call display feature of my phone.

"Crap," I exclaimed. "I guess I spoke too soon. My guess is Button is down again."

Shirley was loud enough to be heard by Kevin as she effused, "You are a miracle worker, Ali! Button is running around, eating, happy, and completely cured! I was so sure I was saying goodbye to her today. Bless you!"

Had my injuries prevented my return that week, Button would have perished. I was once more humbled by the power of chiropractic.

The kids are good at reminding me about the benefits of chiropractic. After a childhood of nonchalant assumptions that their father would adjust them whenever a sore neck, poorly moving knee, or achy low back plagued them, they were launched into a world where chiropractic was difficult to access when they left home. When they get home from university, a request for an adjustment always follows the first welcoming hug. Four of my nieces and nephews, and most recently my daughter Savannah, are electing to follow their university training with four more intensive years of study at chiropractic college.

"I hate seeing injuries and ailments that I know are so easy to fix with an adjustment, and being impotent to deliver it," Savannah summarized.

With an agenda of not orphaning my patients again, I navigate life a little differently now. I wear Yaktrax, elasticated grippers that cover boots to provide ice traction, whenever there is a hint of ice outside. I hold banisters when I descend stairs. I have zero interest in ever testing my bone strength with another fall. I have abandoned my patients too often and spent much of the last weeks promising to not fall again.

A birthday post by a friend alerted me to the bleak fact that Shoppers Drug Mart now welcomes us to enjoy discounts as senior citizens at the young age of fifty-five. Despite reaching that milestone this fall, I will not be pulling out my driver's license this year to qualify yet. I am not saving my bones for reasons of ageing.

I need my bones and muscles for further adventures. The time at home afforded me way too much Google time researching fun options. In the fall, Kevin has signed up for a sculling marathon on Loch Ness and I have enrolled in the Loch Ness Running Marathon one week later.

There are so many epic races begging to be tackled. There is the Russian-border-to-Swedish-border 400-kilometre cross-county ski race in Finland, the Rajalta Rajalle that Kevin, Savannah, and I have firmly in our sights (the boys notably less so). I would like to cross this country by bike and canoe on the recently completed Canada's Great Trail system. We have plans to hike the Kerry Way, a 220-kilometre mountainous trek in Ireland as a family adventure. I have many routes to bike on my road bike, once I have repaired the broken pieces of the front wheel resulting from the bear escapade. And finally, it is just possible … (Kevin don't read this) … that there is yet another Ironman in my future.

About the Author

Photo © by Deb Gleason

D r. Alison Seely started her career as a marine biologist and then shifted to a life of animal care as a veterinarian specializing in animal chiropractic. She adjusts the spines of dogs, horses, and cats, as well as the rare cow, iguana, and even the occasional squirrel. She continues to marvel at the health benefits she witnesses in her varied patient load. Dr. Seely has lectured on animal chiropractic in Canada, the U.S., and abroad.

Alison lives on a small lake in the Ottawa valley with her husband Kevin and massive dog Haka. Although she and Kevin are officially empty nested, they find they are often setting the breakfast table for five or more as their open door is always welcoming lengthy visits from their three children as well as nephews and nieces.

Alison is passionate about fitness. While winters find her cross-country-skiing in the company of Haka, summers are for triathlon and long runs. She has completed ten Ironman competitions, and fifteen marathons.

Although her unbridled enthusiasm for activity has been known to cause her more than her fair share of visits to emergency, she endeavours to remain injury free, out of trouble, and available to those 4-legged creatures that need her most.

Scott Mooney & Jess Clouthier

Made in the USA
Middletown, DE
29 January 2020